Field Book 18

How Many Deer?

A Field Guide to Estimating Deer Population Size

Brenda A. Mayle, Andrew J. Peace
and Robin M. A. Gill
Forest Research

Edinburgh: Forestry Commission

ISBN 0 85538 405 0
FDC 153: 149.6 (410)

KEYWORDS: Census, Fallow deer, Forestry, Muntjac deer, Population
estimation, Populations, Red deer, Roe deer, Sika deer, Wildlife
management

Acknowledgements

The authors would like to thank the many people involved at various
stages during the planning and production of this book: Stephen Buckland
and Simon Hodge for comments on earlier drafts of the manuscript; James
Cordery and Colin Lavin for providing examples for a number of methods
in addition to text comments; the Deer Commission for Scotland for
providing information and the area map for open hill counts, and results
from distance pellet group sampling; the Ministry of Agriculture, Fisheries
and Food for allowing reference to work funded by them; George Gate and
John Williams for photographic material and artwork; June Bell and Mavis
Peacock for typing drafts of the text. Particular thanks go to the Forest
Enterprise ranger staff who have supported the field work for this
publication, and especially those who have monitored faecal pellet decay
in the sites given in Appendix 7.

Enquiries relating to this publication should be addressed to:

The Research Communications Officer
Forest Research
Alice Holt Lodge
Wrecclesham, Farnham
Surrey GU10 4LH

Front cover: *top left* Group of fallow does in birch woodland [FOREST LIFE
PICTURE LIBRARY: 1005495020]. *top right* Roe doe in a woodland ride [FOREST
LIFE PICTURE LIBRARY 1012420020]. *bottom left* Sika stag in a spruce
plantation [NORMAN HEALY]. *bottom right* Red deer on the open hill
[ALASTAIR BAXTER]. *centre* Muntjac doe in a grassy ride [IAN WYLLIE].

Back cover: Searching for faecal pellet groups in an open grassy habitat
within Kielder Forest [TECHNICAL DEVELOPMENT BRANCH, FOREST RESEARCH].

Contents

Preface

Within Great Britain and across much of the Northern hemisphere deer populations have been expanding in size and distribution. In Britain this has been enhanced by an increase in the proportion of woodland cover, and hence suitable habitat for deer. There has also been insufficient recognition by land owners and managers of the need to limit deer numbers. The management of deer populations is a complicated subject with no two sites being exactly the same. To be most effective, detailed knowledge of the deer population range, size, rates of change and habitat use are required before decisions about management objectives and methods are made.

This Field Book aims to provide information on the various methods available for determining deer population size, and the suitability of each method for a given situation. Although aimed primarily at woodland deer managers, methods suitable for a range of situations are described. Results from research by the authors and their coll-eagues, information in the avail-able literature, and the practical experiences of friends and coll-eagues in the field are all drawn together and used as examples to illustrate methods. Methods of greatest use to practising deer managers (in terms of time and cost effectiveness) are described in more detail. The authors hope that the combination of experience, research and observations that make up this Field Book will help to promote sound deer management and encourage those new to the subject to approach it in an informed and objective manner.

The book is divided into four key sections and a fifth section comprising supporting material. Section 1 considers the need to manage deer and the importance of estimating the size of deer populations. In Section 2 guidance is given on choosing a suitable census and sampling method, with emphasis on the importance of establishing initially the underlying objectives of the required survey(s).

Section 3 describes the population estimation methods, numbered 1 to 21, and includes guidance on selection of the most appropriate method. Each follows the format: *Method, Data recorded, Equipment required* and *Health and safety (H & S) considerations, Advantages* and *Disadvantages*. Guidance on the ease of use, performance and levels of costs associated with each method is given in Table 3.1 and within each description. A worked example is provided in most cases. The examples given can be calculated using a simple pocket calculator. Results are presented as deer densities per 100 hectares (or per square kilometre, km^{-2}). Software is available from the authors at Forest Research, Alice Holt Lodge, Wrecclesham, Farnham, Surrey GU10 4LH, to help speed up some of the calculations.

Section 4 reinforces the advantages of using census data in the development of effective deer management strategies. The sup-porting information in Section 5 includes guidance on identification, assessment and recording; example record forms and addresses of equipment suppliers are also provided.

List of plates

List of figures

List of tables

1 The Need to Manage Deer

Within Great Britain and across much of the Northern hemisphere deer populations have been expanding in size and distribution (Gill, 1990; Harris *et al.*, 1995). This has been enhanced by changes in land-use practices which have led to an increase in the proportion of woodland cover, and hence suitable habitat for deer. There has also been insufficient recognition by landowners and managers of the need to actively manage deer. Hence populations have increased in both numbers and distribution, such that deer of one species or another occur in almost every 10 km square of Great Britain (Figure 1.1). Despite

Figure 1.1 *Deer presence in the UK. (Prepared by H. Arnold, J. Gaunt and A. Morton, ITE, Monks Wood)*

1

being our largest land mammal their secretive nature and tendency to avoid humans makes them very difficult to observe, even at high densities. There is generally, therefore, a lack of awareness of the size or density of deer populations in many areas.

As woodland habitats are increasingly planted close to urban areas, the potential for contact with and conflict between human and deer populations increases, emphasising the need for proactive management.

The management of deer populations is a complex subject with no two sites being exactly the same. To be most effective it requires detailed knowledge of the deer population range, size, rates of change and habitat use, before decisions are made about management objectives and how to achieve them. For populations which reside exclusively in one particular area or habitat type it will be easier to define the range, for example where the population is held in a deer park, within an area bounded by an intact deer fence or within the boundaries of a large woodland. Seasonal movements of the deer also need to be taken into account when defining the boundaries of a 'deer range'.

For populations ranging across large areas of land, decisions on management objectives for the whole population may need to be made within a consortium of landowners and managers across whose land the deer roam. This will invariably include people with diverse interests and objectives, from farmers with crop damage, conservation site managers with problems in maintaining particular habitats to owners and managers with sporting interests. The 'Deer Initiative', a partnership of organisations in England and Wales led by the Forestry Commission, aims to encourage responsible and humane management of deer (Forestry Commission, 1995), and the formation of co-operative management groups where necessary.

Why count deer?

The main reasons for estimating the size of a deer population are:

- To determine whether the population is increasing, stable or in decline.
- To identify the level of culling the population can sustain.

Anyone wishing to establish new woodlands will need to know which species are present and at least an index (i.e. an indication) of numbers of deer when deciding whether protection against deer damage is necessary. For example, individual tree protection (e.g. tree guards) against fallow, red and sika deer needs to be 1.8 m tall, while to protect against roe and muntjac browsing, 1.2 m is adequate. Using the incorrect height of protection will lead to greater costs if lower protection would have been adequate, or loss of leading shoots, deformed trees and even replanting if taller protection should have been used.

At very low deer densities (<5 km^{-2}) the risks of damage will be low (especially for large areas of planting). Damage risk generally increases with increasing deer presence, but is influenced by species-specific behaviour and habitat. For example, fallow deer are a herding species and move around their range in large groups. They may cause high impact within a very short period of time by feeding on newly established or coppiced trees or by trampling and lying on agricultural crops.

For managers who are considering cropping a deer population to produce a regular income it will be important to know the sex-class and age-class ratios and rate of increase of the population as well as the population size. Census sampling methods that provide this information and an indication of the accuracy of the population estimate to be calculated will be required.

Accurate methods of estimating the population size will also be required by those wishing to reduce a population. This may be necessary for a number of reasons:

- To reduce crop or woodland damage.
- To decrease levels of road traffic accidents occurring in the area.
- To improve the quality of the herd.

Without an accurate estimate of population size and its rate of increase, it will not be possible to determine how many deer need to be removed to either hold the population stable or reduce it in size.

2 Choosing a Suitable Census and Sampling Method

Objectives

The success of any survey to estimate deer population size should be judged against the underlying objectives. Furthermore, **clear objective setting is essential for the selection of the most appropriate census method and choice of sampling design**. The questions to be answered must be clear at the outset. For example:

- How many deer are there in a specific woodland block?
- How accurate will this answer be for a fixed cost?
- Are estimates required for different habitat types?
- Is the deer population increasing or decreasing?
- Is an *index* of deer numbers, rather than an actual count, acceptable in deciding this?

An index can be thought of as a measurement related to the actual number of deer present, such as the number of deer tracks in snow, and can be extremely useful for broad decision making. Where there is little concern about current population size, or impact levels, or the likelihood of expansion, methods providing only a minimum estimate may be acceptable.

Once the objectives of the study have been decided it should be possible to match these to one of the several population estimation methods described in Section 3, and quantify the amount and type of data that will need to be collected.

The choice between *direct* and *indirect* methods of assessing deer numbers will also be influenced by the objectives. If these include an assessment of age-class or sex-class ratios then direct methods will have to be used. In a forest habitat where direct observation is severely restricted then indirect methods will provide a greater opportunity to estimate deer populations or at least provide an index of their numbers.

Often a quick answer is required but quick methods of estimating deer populations usually involve a number of assumptions which may not be valid for the particular population in question. In general, more accurate population estimates require more time to collect, but greater confidence can be placed in them.

If deer numbers are to be monitored over a number of years it is sensible to keep the census and any sampling methods as consistent as possible, using the same census technique and making assessments when conditions are similar, e.g. at the same time of the year, under similar weather conditions, using the same observers. All this will help to reduce any *bias*, although significant changes in the habitat or disturbance levels over time may affect deer behaviour and presence and hence the suitability of any particular method. Results should be stored so that they are readily retrieved, accessible and clearly understood by others in the future.

Key points
- Make a list of objectives and questions to be answered.
- Select a suitable census method and sampling design to produce the answers required.

- Use of inappropriate methods is inefficient, may be costly, and will produce results that are either too detailed, unreliable or not pertinent to the main objectives/ questions.

Sampling

Several census methods require data to be collected by sampling. On a small scale it may be possible to count all the deer inhabiting an isolated woodland, and consequently have no need to sample. However a complete census is generally not feasible, especially in woodlands, and sampling methods will have to be used. Factors which need to be taken into account in choosing a sampling design include the resources available, the accuracy level required and the likelihood of bias.

The sampling methods discussed below apply equally to estimates of deer, their faecal pellets and their tracks.

Relationship between accuracy precision and bias

Once the sampling method and design have been chosen, care should be taken to ensure that all observers follow the instructions given. The aim is to obtain a result that is precise, accurate and unbiased. Deviation from the chosen method and sampling design may cause the final result to become imprecise, inaccurate and biased, resulting in a waste of time and money.

Precision, accuracy and bias can be defined as follows:

- **Precision** is the closeness of repeated estimates to each other.
- **Accuracy** refers to the closeness of the estimated mean to the true value.
- **Bias** is a systematic component of error, such as observer bias.

Figure 2.1 shows four possible scenarios that can occur when sampling.

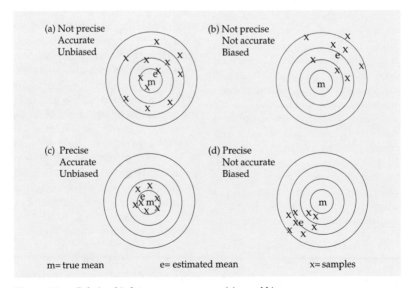

Figure 2.1   *Relationship between accuracy, precision and bias*

Figure 2.1a shows a successful sampling design where the average of the samples (e) gives a good estimate of the true mean (m). Figure 2.1c is the most desirable result (precise and accurate) as a good estimate of the true mean can be obtained from fewer samples with a resultant saving in sampling costs. Figures 2.1b and 2.1d show the effect of bias: the estimated mean for the samples is not close to the actual mean and in these cases the true number of deer are consistently over- or underestimated.

Bias

If bias exists anywhere in the estimation procedure then the estimated deer population size may not be very close to the true size. Increasing the number of sampling units will not remove any bias that is present although it may produce a more precise estimate (Figure 2.1d).

Bias can arise from many sources during the process of estimating deer numbers. During sampling it could be introduced by lack of randomisation of the sample plots or, in a line transect, by deviation from the fixed route to sample a more attractive or accessible habitat type. Mark–resighting methods will be biased if poor capture and marking techniques lead to an increased mortality rate of marked individuals compared to unmarked ones or if the methods assume a *'closed'* deer population during the period between marking and resighting, when it is in fact *'open'* to migration, immigration, mortality and recruitment.

Detection and correction for bias can be extremely difficult. Generally bias in the final population estimate can only be detected by testing the method used on a population of known size. However some simple precautions can be applied during the sampling period. For example, if it is obvious that deer on the outer edges of a strip transect are going undetected then the width of the strip should be reduced. Observer bias can be detected by checking the results from different observers using the same method on the same site. Consistent differences between observers will suggest that bias is occurring but not who is biased. All observers should therefore be retrained. More often than not, the presence or absence of bias will only be confirmed by using a second sampling technique with a further increase in cost. Many of the census techniques listed in this Field Book appear in the scientific literature where the effects of bias have been measured on known deer populations. Many papers suggest methods that can measure the extent of any bias and some produce models that convert biased results to unbiased estimates of the population size.

Ultimately, if bias persists in the deer population estimate then there are several options. In the worst case the chosen sampling method must be replaced with a more suitable method to control the particular circumstances causing the bias, and the results already obtained must be rejected. Alternatively it may be acceptable to use the biased estimate as an index of the true population number. This decision will depend on the amount of observed bias, the value of having at least some idea of the population size, and the consequence of any wrong decisions made as a result of using a false estimate of population size. For the methods described we highlight factors which may lead to bias.

The precision of unbiased estimates of a deer population can be improved by increasing sampling intensity. However a gain in precision will nearly always come at a cost. By comparing relative precision and cost the surveyor can make important decisions on whether the planned level of resources are sufficient to provide a precise enough estimate and hence reduce the likelihood of wasting resources on a study that either fails to deliver sufficiently precise results or produces overly precise results. Even decisions on whether or not to carry out a survey at all can be made based on the expected precision for a given cost.

Key points
- Avoid introducing bias during the sampling procedure.
- Increasing the sample size will increase precision but may not deal with bias or improve accuracy.
- Most surveys will involve a compromise between cost, accuracy and precision.

Sample size

At an early stage of the design a decision must be made about *'How large a sample is required to achieve a given precision?'*. Too small a sample will produce an estimate that is too imprecise to be useful, while a sample that is too large is both inefficient and costly. Recommended sample sizes are given for each census method that requires a sampling design. For the reader who is familiar with statistical techniques, books on sampling theory, such as Cochran (1977), give formulae to estimate sample sizes for a given precision.

Most projects are undertaken with a fixed budget and this may limit the size of the sample that can be taken. Studies will consist of fixed costs, such as administration and planning, and a cost for each sampling unit. The maximum sample size one can afford to take is calculated as follows:

$$\text{Maximum sample size} = \frac{\text{Total budget - Fixed costs}}{\text{Cost of each sampling unit}}$$

If this maximum sample size is bigger than the number that is needed to achieve the required precision then there is no problem. There is no point in taking more observations than necessary to achieve the desired precision. If the maximum sample size is smaller than the number needed for the specified precision, then there are three possible choices:
- Take as many observations as can be afforded, knowing the results will not be as precise as hoped for.
- Use a different, cheaper sampling design which is more likely to give the required precision.
- Do not carry out the survey.

Probability sampling

The sampling methods listed below use the concept of *probability sampling*. In order to apply this concept the study area for which the deer population is to be estimated has to be defined and subdivided into equal sized units called *sampling units*. These sampling units (which, for example, could be 7 m x 7 m quadrats, 2 m x 100 m strips or 1 hectare plots), should be distinct, non-overlapping and together constitute the whole study area. They then form the basis for the selection of the sample.

If faced with a choice between different sampling units then a guiding rule is to try to select one that returns the greatest precision for the available resources. *Generally, the precision of the overall estimate of the deer population is related to the square root of the number of sampling units selected for the sample. To double the precision of the estimate the number of units selected must be quadrupled.* For a fixed sample size, say 5% of the total study area, fewer larger sampling units will normally give less accurate results than more smaller sampling units. However, it is generally cheaper to sample a larger sampling unit than a smaller one. If sampling units are too small, numbers may be biased by *edge effects* (observers may tend to include all individuals that straddle the sample boundary). One solution is to choose square sampling units which have a smaller edge to area ratio than rectangular plots.

Simple random sampling

Simple random sampling is a method in which the sampling units are chosen independently and with equal probability. If there is prior knowledge of the variability between sampling units, such as certain habitat types being more likely to give higher responses than others, then simple random sampling will not give the best results. One of the methods described later may be more precise.

Choosing a simple random sample is usually done using random numbers which are obtained from a computer or random number table (Appendix 1). A random number table is just a list of digits 0,1,2...9 where the number at any point in the table has been chosen at random so that each digit has exactly the same chance of appearing in any position.

Example

Suppose a forest block is divided into 500 equally sized plots (sampling units) and each plot is uniquely identified by a number from 1 to 500. To take a random sample of 10 plots first choose a random starting position in the random number table and combine the digits in a long string, say 173649374655238475601374110 ... .

As the largest plot number is 500, which has 3 digits, group the random numbers into groups of three: 173 649 374 655 238 475 601 374 110 ... .

Plot 173 is the first plot in the sample.
Plot 649 is ignored as there is no plot with this number.
Plot 374 is the second plot in the sample.
Plot 655 is ignored.
Plots 238 and 475 are the third and fourth plots in the sample.
Plot 601 is ignored.
Plot 374 is a repeat and is ignored.
Plot 110 is the fifth plot in the sample.
Continue until 10 plots have been selected.

Results from the sample are used to calculate four important statistics:

- The sample mean
  – average count per plot
- The sample variance
  – a measure of variability between plot counts
- The standard error of the mean
  – a measure of precision with which the population mean is estimated
- Approximate 95% confidence interval of the mean

– a measure of precision with which the population mean is estimated.

Now if 5, 4, 2, 6, 8, 3, 4, 6, 5, and 7 deer are observed in the 10 plots the following information is normally calculated from the sample data.

The sample mean
The mean number of deer per sampling unit

$$= \frac{\text{Sum of all sample deer}}{\text{Number of sample plots}}$$

$$= \frac{5 + 4 + 2 + ... + 7}{10}$$

$$= 5 \text{ deer}$$

The sample variance
The variance of deer per sampling unit

$$= \frac{\text{Sum (samples - sample mean)}^2}{\text{Number of sample plots - 1}}$$

$$= \frac{(5-5)^2 + (4-5)^2 + (2-5)^2 + ... + (7-5)^2}{10-1}$$

$$= \frac{30}{9}$$

$$= 3.33 \text{ deer}$$

The standard error of the mean (s.e.)
The standard error of the mean number of deer per sampling unit

$$= \sqrt{\frac{\text{Variance of deer per sampling plot}}{\text{Number of sample plots}}}$$

$$= \sqrt{\frac{3.33}{10}}$$

$$= 0.58 \text{ deer}$$

Approximate 95% confidence interval of the mean (95% CI)

$$= \text{sample mean} \pm 2 \times \text{s.e}$$

$$= 5 \pm 1.16$$

$$= 3.84 - 6.16 \text{ deer}$$

The 95% confidence interval can be interpreted as follows: we are 95% confident that the true population mean of the 500 sampling units lies between 3.84 and 6.16 deer per sampling unit. Sometimes 80% confidence intervals are used and are approximated as follows:

$$80\% \text{ CI} = \text{sample mean} \pm 1.3 \times \text{s.e.}$$

Within simple random sampling the selection of the sample is left to chance and any prior knowledge of differences in deer numbers within the study area is ignored. However, this knowledge can be used to increase the precision obtained for a fixed number of samples by using a *stratified* sampling design.

Stratified sampling
Where there is likely to be variation across the study area in the factors being measured (e.g. different decay rates of pellet groups in different habitats or variation in visibility of deer depending on tree species and age-class) it is important to stratify. To do this, the study area, consisting of varied sampling units is divided into strata, each of which contains a group of similar sampling units. A simple random sample is taken independently from each stratum (as above) and the total population estimate calculated by combining the estimate of the stratum means. As sample size can vary between strata this provides scope for allocating resources between strata and in a number of cases leads to a gain in precision.

Table 2.1 *Habitat structure classes based on differences in vegetation and cover*

Habitat class	Top height	Resources available to deer
Establishment/ restock	1 m	Increasing food availability. Little cover/shelter.
Pre-thicket	1-3 m	High food quality and abundance. Increasing cover.
Thicket	3-10 m	Canopy closure and reducing food availability except where gaps in trees occur. Excellent cover.
Pole-stage	10+ m	Poor food availability except where gaps occur. Cover good depending on thinning level.
Pre-felling	10+ m	In open crops food good as ground cover increases. Cover from disturbance good, but from weather may be poor.
Open ground	No crop	Food variable depending on availability of herb/shrubby species. Shelter poor but topography may be sufficient for smaller deer species.

Stratification is normally based on habitat or ecological features with which deer density is likely to be correlated. Decisions can be made from large scale vegetation or habitat maps of the study area. Tables 2.1 and 2.2 show different woodland habitat strata determined from the availability of food and shelter for the deer. Table 2.2 shows the potential range of open and woodland habitat strata. Within each of the structure classes it may be necessary to subdivide the strata using specific knowledge of the site or deer population. Some areas may have high visitor access or other disturbances such as game shooting while other areas may include rutting stands at specific times of the year. Forestry operations other than clearfelling, however, do not often cause high levels of disturbance to the deer or lead to unusual behavioural patterns. Appendix 2

(after Ratcliffe and Mayle, 1992) gives an example of site stratification for Alice Holt Forest in North Hampshire/Surrey. Stratification was based on crop structure classes and types in preparation for faecal pellet counts and undertaken by someone with no previous knowledge of the site.

In stratified sampling, sampling units should be allocated to strata based on the variability (*variance*) that is expected within each stratum. Strata with greater than average variation should be allocated proportionally more sampling units. Similarly, if sampling costs vary from stratum to stratum, then the more expensive it is to sample a stratum, the fewer the number of sampling units should be allocated to it, down to a minimum sample size. This concept can be solved mathematically and is known as

10

Table 2.2 *Habitat stratification based on vegetation structure classes*

Open habitat	Woodland habitat	
Bare ground	Establishment/Restock	
Grass ride/glade	*Conifer*	*Broadleaved*
Riparian	Pre-thicket	Pre-thicket
Moor/heath	Thicket	Thicket
Arable crops	Pole-stage	Pole-stage
Grass pasture	Pre-fell	Pre-fell
	Mature/retention	Mature/retention
		Short rotation coppice

Shrub and ground vegetation below conifer and broadleaved tree crops on the same site are likely to differ due to the differential effect of shading and so stratification needs to consider crop species.

optimum allocation. We will introduce and recommend the use of *proportional allocation* which, on most occasions, is nearly as efficient as optimum allocation. In fact the two methods become equivalent when costs and variability are similar between strata. Proportional allocation can be defined as follows:

A method of selecting samples from different strata such that the numbers chosen from the strata are proportional to the population sampling units in those strata.

Example

We wish to estimate the total number of roe deer faecal pellet groups in a study area of 5 ha (50 000 m^2) to within 20% of the true total with 95% confidence. If we choose a sampling unit of 50 m^2 then there are 1000 possible sampling units in total. In this study area there are three distinct habitat types which are known to influence deer use: habitat A covers 2 ha, habitat B 2 ha and habitat C 1 ha. With expected differences in habitat use, stratified sampling would appear to be the most appropriate sampling method. Applying proportional allocation

we will allocate 2/5 of the samples to habitat A, 2/5 of the samples to habitat B and 1/5 of the samples to habitat C.

How many sampling units should be sampled? Table 3.5 (page 47) suggests a sample size of 35 if we have a high density roe deer population and we require the estimate to be within 20% of the true total with 95% confidence. (An initial site visit to determine an index of population size may be necessary before decisions on required sample sizes can be made.)

Therefore 14 samples are taken from habitat A, 14 from habitat B and 7 from habitat C.

Counts of deer pellets per plot are:

habitat A 3,1,5,4,2,0,3,4,4,5,2,0,5,4

habitat B 3,5,4,6,5,2,3,6,4,0,3,6,7,2

habitat C 0,2,1,4,2,4,1

We then calculate the mean and variance for each stratum using the equations described previously.

	Number of sampling units	Number of sample plots	Mean number of pellet groups	Variance
Habitat A	400	14	3.0	3.08
Habitat B	400	14	3.0	3.85
Habitat C	200	7	2.0	2.33
Total	1000	35		

These results are then combined to give an overall population estimate as follows.

The mean number of faecal groups per plot $= \dfrac{\text{Sum (stratum mean x number of stratum sampling units)}}{\text{Total number of sampling units}}$

$$= \frac{(3.0 \times 400) + (4.0 \times 400) + (2.0 \times 200)}{1000}$$

$$= 3.2 \text{ pellet groups}$$

Standard error of the sample mean

$$= \sqrt{\text{Sum (stratum sampling unit proportion}^2 \text{ x stratum variance/number of stratum sample plots)}}$$

$$= \sqrt{(400/1000)^2 \times 3.08/14 + (400/1000)^2 \times 3.85/14 + (200/1000)^2 \times 2.33/7}$$

$$= 0.30 \text{ pellet groups}$$

So the **estimated total** number of roe deer faecal pellet groups for the 5 ha

= Number of sampling units in the 5 ha x mean number of groups per sampling unit

= 1000 x 3.2

= 3200

With **estimated standard error**

= Number of sampling units in the 5 ha x standard error of the sample mean

= 1000 x 0.30

= 300

and **approximate 95% confidence interval**

= Population total ± 2 x population standard error

= 3200 ± 600

= 2600 - 3800

This study has achieved its objective. The true number of faecal pellet groups lies within 20% of our estimated total of 3200 with 95% confidence.

Other sampling methods

In most cases the appropriate choice of simple random sampling or stratified sampling will lead to an efficient, if not optimal, estimation of the deer population. However there are a number of other sampling methods such as cluster sampling and two-stage sampling that could be used in their place. For a fixed cost, the precision obtained by these methods depends, as in the above sampling methods, on both the variability between sampling units and sub-units and the costs of sampling them. Details of these calculations are not given in this Field Book but can be obtained from any sampling textbook; see for example: Cochran, 1977; Levy and Lemeshow, 1991; Thompson, 1992.

Key points

- Divide the study area into sampling units and sample using the concept of probability sampling.
- The size of sampling unit should be large enough to record sufficient individuals but small enough to increase precision for a fixed cost.
- In simple random sampling, the sample size needed to give results to a given precision is dependent on the variability between sampling units.
- Stratified sampling is preferred to simple random sampling if the population of sampling units is heterogeneous but can be subdivided into parts (strata) which are fairly homogeneous.
- If sampling costs and within strata variability are similar across strata then sample using proportional allocation.

Line transects

Sampling using line transects is unlike the finite population sampling theory described above as the size of the sampling area does not need to be known, and during the survey not all deer need to be detected. As the perpendicular distance from an observed animal to the transect line is recorded this method is more commonly known as *distance sampling*.

Line transects should be placed at random within the study area such that there is no relationship between the transect line and the deer, i.e. deer are not avoiding or associating with the line. However, when using this sampling method for direct count census methods, it is usually necessary to use the existing road network, for practical reasons. This provides acceptable results if roads are well distributed across the survey area, and deer are not avoiding or attracted to them. These line transects can be thought of as long narrow quadrats where every deer on or near the centre line of the transect is detected but where deer away from this line will only be detected with a probability that is a function of their perpendicular distance away from it. The probability of observing an individual deer is represented by the detection function which is estimated from the distances. This function is used to calculate deer density using the total length of the transect lines, and the number of deer observed within a set distance, of the transect line. Further details are given in Buckland *et al.* (1993).

If deer occur in groups then the distance to the centre of the group should be recorded together with the number of individuals in the group. Average group size in the population can then be estimated and the density of individuals computed by multiplying the density of groups and the average group size. When using this equation it is necessary to check and take into account, any influence of group size on the probability of detection of the group. Larger groups are more likely to be detected than smaller ones. (This can be done using the specialist software mentioned below.)

If detection rates are likely to vary between different parts of the study area then it will be necessary to stratify the area as discussed previously: see Stratified sampling. Densities can be estimated for individual strata and combined to give a total estimate of deer. The computation of the detection function and estimation of population density require the use of specially developed computer programs. The program DISTANCE (available on the Worldwide Web http://www.ruwpa.st-and.ac.uk/distance/) is recommended for these calculations and further details on the theory, sample sizes required and analysis of distance sampling are available in Buckland *et al.* (1993).

Key points
- Transect lines should be independent with respect to the distribution of the deer within the sampling area.
- Perpendicular distances must be measured accurately.
- Adequate analysis cannot be carried out without specialist software.

3 Population Estimation Methods

Population estimation methods, also called census methods, fall into three main categories: direct methods, indirect methods, and the use of cull data. Greater confidence is often placed in methods involving actual observations of deer. However, studies of marked populations and comparisons of different methods have shown that some of the most frequently used direct observation methods are the least accurate in many situations, with only 10–33% of the true population being recorded (Anderson, 1953; Langbein, 1996; Ratcliffe, 1987). For all methods the best, i.e. most accurate, population estimate will be obtained by sampling across the whole range (winter and summer) of the population being considered.

The choice of method to be used will depend upon the following factors:

- Whether an index or an accurate population assessment is required.
- Habitat type: in open habitats deer are generally seen more easily than in wooded habitats.
- Seasonal and daily behaviour patterns which may influence which sex- and age- classes of deer will be found in the area.
- Terrain which may be more suitable for some methods than others.
- The resources available in terms of cash, labour and expertise.
- The timescale in which the information is required.
- The limitations of weather.

The flowchart in Figure 3.1 identifies which method(s) are likely to be most practicable in any given situation, while Table 3.1 provides a quick guide to the performance and costs of each method. This is also provided in a small summary box within each numbered method. Practical limitations of application and potential biases which may influence accuracy are highlighted in each method description under Advantages/Disadvantages, to help the reader choose the most appropriate method.

Direct counts

In some habitats it is possible to see and directly count deer. However, even in open moorland, animals resting in hollows may be easily missed, and deer may take flight before accurate assessments of numbers, age-class and sex-class are made. Counting may be easier when animals are concentrated together in groups, but this may also make accurate assessment of numbers more difficult when group sizes are very large. Dividing the deer range into sections or a grid, and avoiding counting when weather and visibility are poor usually increases precision.

In smaller areas and where it is possible to recognise individual deer, the total number can be estimated over time by keeping a record of the different individuals seen on each visit. Eventually no new animals will be seen (unless new animals are constantly entering the population through births and immigration) and the list of individuals will equal the population size. However, for most deer species it is difficult to confidently tell individuals apart without additional marking unless very many hours are spent carefully observing and recording individual features.

In wooded areas it is particularly difficult to observe and identify individuals and there will be animals which are rarely (if ever) seen. To be confident about population estimates based on observations, a large number of individual observations are required. Approximately 5 separate sightings of each individual deer are required before the observer can be 90% confident about the total population estimate. For example if 10 individual deer have been seen, observations need to be continued until there are 50 separate observations.

Methods which allow the unobserved part of the population to be estimated are more efficient in terms of time. Mark–resighting techniques are a way of determining this, but catching and marking deer is an extremely expensive and time-consuming operation, and hence these techniques are generally only used for research.

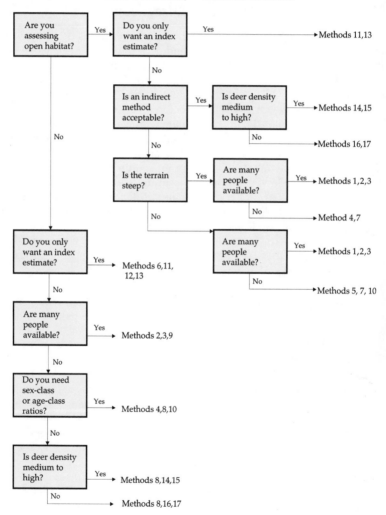

Figure 3.1 *Flowchart for selecting appropriate census method*

16

Table 3.1   *Suitability of census methods to estimate deer population size*

Census/count method	Performance as an estimate	Performance as an index	Inexpensive equipment costs	Inexpensive labour costs	Simple data analysis	Data collection period
1. Open hill	*****	*****	***	*	*****	1–7 days
2. Drive counts	***	***	***	*	****	1–7 days
3. Static census	***	****	****	*	****	1–3 days
4. Vantage point	***	****	****	*****	****	1–7 days
5. Aerial counts	****	*****	*	****	***	1–2 days
6. Spotlight counts	**	***	***	****	***	1–7 days
7. Thermal imaging: direct counts	*****	*****	**	****	*****	1–3 days
8. Thermal imaging: distance sampling	*****	*****	**	****	*	3–5 days
9. Mark–resighting	****	****	*	*	**	3–24 months
10. Change-in-ratio counts	***	****	***	***	***	6–9 months
11. Impact levels	*	***	***	***	***	1–5 days (crop) 6–12 months (habitat)
12. Track/slot counts	*	***	*****	*****	****	1–4 days
13. Faecal pellet index	*	****	*****	*****	****	1–4 days
14. Faecal pellet clearance	*****	*****	*****	**	****	2–3 months
15. Faecal pellet standing crop	****	*****	*****	***	***	4–12 months
16. Faecal pellet strip transects	***	****	*****	***	****	4–12 months
17. Faecal pellet line transects	****	*****	*****	***	*	4–12 months
18. Balance sheet	**	***	***	**	***	6–9 months
19. Life tables	***	****	****	**	**	5+ years
20. Cohort analysis	****	****	*****	**	**	5+ years
21. Population modelling	*****	*****	***	**	**	1+ years

Note Methods 18-21 require information from previous culls.

Key
  *****   excellent
  ****   good
  ***   fair
  **   poor
  *   very poor

Direct counts may be carried out by day, or by night with the aid of spotlights or night vision equipment, and may involve few or many people. The section that follows describes the most useful methods.

Daylight counts

1. Open hill counts

The Deer Commission for Scotland (DCS) uses this technique to count red deer and, where they occur on open hills, sika deer populations (Stewart, 1976).

Method

The whole of the red deer range in Scotland is divided into 49 discrete blocks (Figure 3.2), each encompassing the winter and summer ranges of both stags and hinds. The perimeter of each block should have natural or man-made barriers sufficiently substantial to ensure there is relatively little interchange of animals between neighbouring blocks (e.g. deer fences, lochs, roads and railways).

Each block is subdivided into sections (bounded by prominent physical features such as rivers and high ridges), and each can easily be covered by a census team in a day. Block size depends upon the number of members in the counting team (usually 8-10). Experienced counters can cover 1200–2000 hectares in a day.

Counts are carried out in late winter and early spring (January–April) when the deer have been driven onto low ground by snow cover. They are usually in their poorest physical condition and so do not move far during the day. Classification is also easiest at this time.

Team members should have binoculars (minimum of 7 x magnification and 30 mm objective), a telescope

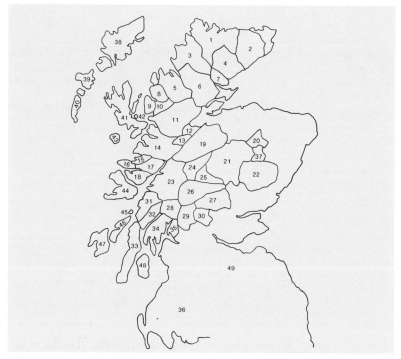

Figure 3.2 *Deer Commission for Scotland: red deer count areas. Blocks 31–36 and 49 are unsuitable for open hill counts*

(x 20–25), a pocket radio, a notebook and a 1 inch (1 : 50 000) Ordnance Survey map with their own and adjacent areas clearly indicated. As the count team move through the sections they observe and record the number of stags, hinds and calves in each group, the time of observation, the direction of movement and any particularly recognisable animals (outstandingly good or bad heads, hummels or injured animals). Movements of animals into neighbouring sections should be reported by radio to neighbouring counters to reduce the likelihood of double counting.

On open ground where deer can be observed easily without disturbance and without causing them to group up with other animals, counters can work individually. However in broken ground or scrub woodland they should work in pairs: one observing and recording from a suitable vantage point, the other moving the deer. When disturbed, individual deer tend to herd and this facilitates counting. During periods of severe weather when large numbers of deer (up to 1000) tend to herd together on lower ground, counters should work in pairs, preferably splitting the deer into groups of approximately 200 to count, and cross-check each other's results.

Counters should work down or across wind so that disturbed animals tend to move onto areas already counted. The finishing line for the day's count should be kept as short as possible to reduce the likelihood of deer already accounted for moving onto the adjacent area to be counted the next day or vice versa. The following day's count is started at the previous day's finishing point. Counters' records should be checked and collated at the end of each day, and any possible double counts eliminated. Counting is continued until the whole block is completed, and the results from each day are collated to provide an overall estimate of population size, age-class and sex-class ratios for the block.

Data recorded   Numbers of animals, by sex- and age-class, in each group, time observed and direction of movement.

Equipment required   Binoculars, telescope, pocket radio, notebook, compass, 1 : 50 000 Ordnance Survey maps of area.

H & S considerations   Ensure team members suitably dressed for prevailing weather conditions (risk of exposure in open habitats in late winter).

Advantages
- Suitable for very large areas.
- Probably one of the most reliable methods.
- Species composition, sex- and age-class ratios can be determined.

Disadvantages
- Only applicable to open or mainly open ground.
- Requires good visibility.
- Only a minimum population size can be estimated.
- Precision cannot be determined and influenced by observer bias in sex- and age-class classification (~10% red deer stags and up to 30% calves misclassified as hinds; Lowe, 1969).
- Results specific to count days, and liable to influences of seasonal changes in climate and deer behaviour.

- Large numbers of people required for a number of consecutive days.
- Requires careful, detailed organisation.
- Blocks are counted only every 5–10 years.

Performance as an estimate	*****
Performance as an index	*****
Inexpensive equipment costs	***
Inexpensive labour costs	*
Simple data analysis	*****
Data collection period	1–7 days

Example 1

An area of open hill approximately 10 x 30 km was counted over two consecutive days during January by a 10-man team of DCS staff and local stalkers. It was divided into eight subareas (a–h). The results are shown in Table 3.2. There was wide variation in the number of animals counted in each block with almost 50% of the whole population being counted in block a. The total population estimate for the whole area was 530 stags, 802 hinds and 336 red deer calves.

Table 3.2 *Results from open hill counts*

Subarea	Stags	Hinds	Calves
a	338	353	156
b	2	4	1
c	28	41	16
d	96	178	67
e	8	11	5
f	2	16	9
g	50	199	82
h	6	0	0
Total	530	802	336

Example 2

Larger areas may require subdividing into 25 or more subareas. Even with large numbers of DCS and local stalkers it is often not possible to count such blocks within a few days and inclement or unsuitable weather will often delay or interrupt counts such that a 30 x 50 km block may be counted over 8–10 days within a 30-day period. Care must be taken to ensure that animals have not moved from previously counted to uncounted areas. One such area was counted during March–April 1994 and totals were 3825 stags, 6925 hinds and 1325 red deer calves.

2. Drive counts

Method

The area to be counted should be clearly identified on 1:10 000 map. Large numbers of observers are positioned around and within the area to be counted, such that each person only views in one direction and is able to see to the next observer (Figure 3.3). Each observer has a map specifying the area they are to observe and the position of neighbouring observers. A beat team then moves gently through the area to move animals out of cover to enable them to be counted. Beaters should be spaced about 10 m apart and be able to see the person either side of them. Observers record details of animals moving out of cover as specified, including time and direction of movement. Members of the beat team also record animals seen moving back past them, to one side only.

Individually recognisable animals are recorded, as a means of identifying specific individuals or groups and reducing double counting.

The operation should be co-ordinated from a high spot providing as wide a view over the area as possible to enable the beat line to be directed via pocket radios, particularly through woodland habitats. At the end of the operation all records are collected and the minimum population size calculated, using details of individual animals, time of sighting and direction of movement to ensure that double counting is minimised.

This method is more successful for small woodland blocks and for larger species such as red deer than for the smaller species (roe and muntjac) which are more difficult to flush from cover or classify when moving at speed.

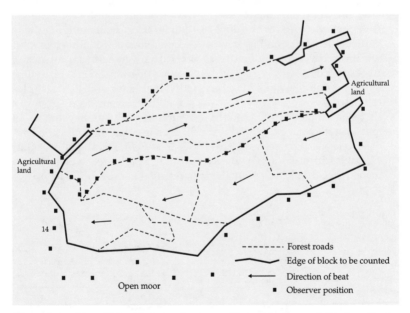

Figure 3.3 *Map of drive count area showing positions of observers and direction of beat; 14 refers to observer number 14 (see Figure 3.4)*

Data recorded For each observer and beater, numbers of animals seen, by species, sex- and age-class, time of observation and direction of travel.

Equipment required Maps of the area, indicating observer positions and viewing area (Figure 3.3), and record forms (Figure 3.4); radios and whistles for beaters.

H & S considerations Potential for beaters to become lost in thick cover, particularly in large areas. Bright clothing and roll-calls reduce risk.

Advantages
- Suitable for small or large areas.
- Suitable for open ground and woodlands.
- Species composition, sex- and age-class ratios can be estimated.
- Completed in 1 day.

Disadvantages
- Requires good visibility on the day.
- Deer are very difficult to flush from cover (even with dogs) particularly adults; and juveniles remain in cover for the first few weeks of life.
- Only minimum population size estimated.
- Precision cannot be determined and accuracy is influenced by observer bias in age- and sex-class classification (e.g. young males recorded as females

especially when no antler growth present; Winder, unpublished).
- Results specific to count day, liable to influences of seasonal behaviour, weather and disturbance prior to and on the day.
- Large numbers of people (60–120) required as observers and beaters.
- Requires careful, detailed organisation.
- Large numbers of beaters are difficult to co-ordinate in thick cover and undulating terrain.

Performance as an estimate	***
Performance as an index	***
Inexpensive equipment costs	***
Inexpensive labour costs	*
Simple data analysis	****
Data collection period	1–7 days

Example

This method has been used to estimate the size of a population of red deer in thicket conifer woodland in south-west England (Winder and Chanin, unpublished). A minimum of 56 observers plus 40 beaters were used for an area of 3 km² (Figure 3.3). Thirty-nine individual hinds and 13 stags (plus 1 roe deer) were seen, giving a minimum population estimate of 52 deer in 3 km² or 17.3 deer km⁻². (Results from faecal pellet counts in the same area suggested a population density of 13 km⁻².)

Figure 3.4 *Drive count record form. Obs point : observation point; cps : cows, ponies, sheep; deer? : species unknown; (?) : sex- or age-class unknown*

J. Holmes. View left & right along track.

Obs point	time	cps stock	Deer ?	RED				ROE			
				M	F	calf	(?)	M	F	Kid	(?)
14	13·50		6	1	3		2	Seen in wood			
	14·00		3		2	1		Seen leaving wood.			
	14·05		1		1			" " "			

Recorded by Eric at 13·52
Crossing stream.
All same animals
1 ♂ + 1 unknown extra.

22

3. Static census

Method

This method is similar to drive counts in that observers are placed at locations around and within the area (woodland block) to be counted prior to the periods of greatest deer activity (dusk and dawn). They observe and record deer as they move out of cover to feed. Observation periods should be a minimum of 2½-3 hours to ensure that animals which may have settled down to ruminate just before the observers arrived will have started feeding again before the observers depart. Observers record sex- and age-class details for all deer seen, their position, time of observation and direction of movement, and any unusual features (to enable double counting to be eliminated). The total number of animals seen (minus any records which are considered to be double counts) indicates the minimum population size. Particularly recognisable animals should be recorded as a means of reducing double counts. The method is most suited to early spring (March/April) when vegetation and cover are limited allowing easier observation of the deer, but it is generally not recommended as a method of assessing overall population size.

Data recorded   Species, sex-class, age-class, time of observation and direction of travel for all animals seen.

Equipment required   Maps of the area, indicating observer positions and viewing area, record forms and binoculars.

H & S considerations   Ensure observers are suitably dressed for prevailing weather (risk of exposure in wintry conditions).

Advantages
- Can be used in all habitat types.
- Species composition, sex- and age-class ratios can be estimated.
- Completed in 1 day.

Disadvantages
- Requires good visibility.
- Only minimum population size can be estimated.
- Accuracy influenced by observer bias in age and sex classification.
- Results specific to 1 day and liable to influences of seasonal behaviour, weather and disturbance levels prior to and on the day.
- Many observers (30–40) required.
- Requires detailed organisation.

Performance as an estimate	***
Performance as an index	****
Inexpensive equipment costs	****
Inexpensive labour costs	*
Simple data analysis	****
Data collection period	1–3 days

Example

A static census in a large forest in North Wales involved 34 observers. They were positioned before dawn and collected 2½-3 hours later. The time, position and direction of movement was recorded for all deer seen (does 1 year+, bucks, fawns and unidentified). Conditions were ideal with calm, dry, cool weather. A minimum of 131 deer were seen (95 does, 14 fawns, 8 bucks and 14 unclassified), but as only 25% of the forest was visible to the observers this was estimated to represent at least 524 deer (19 km^{-2}). Faecal pellet group counts carried out on the same day by the same people, in all habitat types except thicket conifer, indicated 629–895 deer (22–25 km^{-2}) had been using the area over the previous 5 month period (decay length).

23

4. Vantage point counts

This method has been used successfully to determine densities of red, sika and roe deer in coniferous forests in Scotland (Ratcliffe, 1987; Ratcliffe and Mayle, unpublished). As it involves viewing down into an area from a high or 'vantage' point it can only be used in hilly areas.

Method

The area is first identified and stratified (see Sampling in Section 2) into habitats. Randomly selected representative areas of each habitat, suitable for the technique, are identified. These should be large contiguous blocks (40–100 ha) which can be viewed from a suitable vantage point, generally from across or above a valley (Plate 1). At the vantage point the observer first clearly marks on the map the area which can be readily seen and blocks out areas which cannot be viewed into, such as small blocks of different age structure and dead ground in the lee of ridges (Figure 3.5).

The delineated area is methodically scanned using binoculars (7–10 x 50 mm) for any deer movement. A telescope (15–60 x 60 mm) is used to classify any deer located into age-

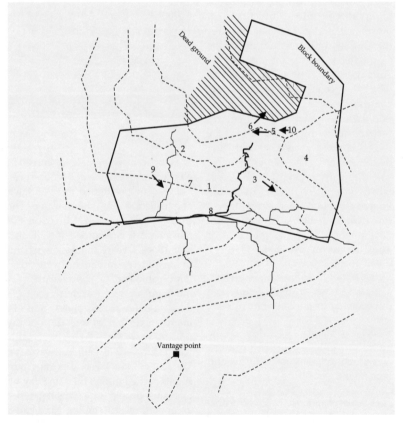

Figure 3.5 *Vantage point count map for Abhain Bheag, Carradale. Numbers 1–10 refer to observed deer (see Figure 3.6). Arrows indicate direction of movement*

24

and sex-classes. This is possible up to distances of 1 km for red or sika deer assuming visibility is good. Roe deer can only be confidently classified up to 0.5 km away. All deer observed and their direction of movement are recorded on the map and the record form (Appendix 3). From a good vantage point deer can be seen moving through even extremely dense habitats, although this may be for only short periods of time as they cross open spaces (such as areas of check, rides, drainsides) within the area. Deer moving into the area from blocks which had initially been identified as not capable of being viewed into should be noted (to prevent double counting) but *not* included in the final estimate.

Watches should last at least 2½ hours to ensure that animals which had settled to ruminate just before the observer arrived are rising to feed again before the watch is completed. At the end of the count period the minimum number of deer seen (taking account of the possibility of observing the same animals more than once as they move in and out of cover) is related to the area being observed and expressed as a density per square kilometre. Three or four counts should be carried out for the same area over consecutive mornings and evenings. The maximum number of deer recorded in the habitat for any single observation period should be used as the habitat specific density estimate, particularly for sedentary species such as roe deer. Ideally other areas representative of the same habitat structure should also be sampled and the habitat specific density calculated as the mean of the densities determined for each representative. This should be repeated for each of the different habitat types in the total

area. Population size can then be estimated from habitat specific densities and knowledge of the area of each habitat in the forest.

Vantage point counts should be carried out when there is limited ground vegetation (March to May). Where there is very little disturbance to the deer during the day, particularly in large woodland blocks, it may be possible to observe deer moving at most times of the day. However, peak deer activity periods tend to be around dusk and dawn, particularly where human disturbance is high and so the most suitable periods for observing deer are 06.00 - 10.00 and 16.00 - 21.00 hours.

If the vantage point is on a ride or track, viewing may be possible from a vehicle. (Care must be taken to ensure that the view is not restricted by the vehicle's internal structure, such as window frames.)

Data recorded   Species, sex- and age-class, and direction of movement of all animals.

Equipment required   Binoculars, telescope, map of area (1:10 000).

H & S considerations   Ensure observer suitably dressed for prevailing weather conditions (risk of exposure if viewing from outside a vehicle in late winter). Preferably two observers present.

Advantages
• Species composition, sex- and age-class ratios can be estimated.
• Seasonal deer use may be indicated by carrying out counts in the same area during different seasons.
• Only 1–2 observers required.

Disadvantages
- Only suitable in hilly terrain.
- Requires good visibility.
- Generally only a minimum population density estimated.
- Precision cannot be determined unless a number of representatives of each habitat are sampled.
- Bias may be introduced if the area observed is not typical of the habitat type being sampled.
- Results are specific to count days and liable to influences of seasonal changes in climate and deer behaviour.

Performance as an estimate	***
Performance as an index	****
Inexpensive equipment costs	****
Inexpensive labour costs	*****
Simple data analysis	****

Data collection period	1–3 days

Example

Vantage point counts to estimate sika deer densities and population size were carried out in an area of east Scotland, during 1988. Figure 3.5 shows an area of thicket observed during one count period; Figure 3.6 is the completed vantage point count record form. During the full 3 hour observation period 14 individual sika deer were seen: 5 adult males, 8 adult females and 1 unclassified. The area observed was 47 ha, so that the density recorded was 29.8 km^{-2}. Three areas of thicket were observed during the morning and evenings over a 2 day period. Estimated densities varied from 12.5 to 29.8 deer km^{-2}.

Forest *Carradale* Conservancy .... Observer(s) *AHC* ....

Location *Abhain Bheag* Area *47* ha Structural Type *Thicket*. Planting Yr ....

Date *26 May 1988* Time on *07:40* .... Time off *10:40* ....

Weather Conditions and Visibility *Poor at start* ....

DEER SEEN									
Time	Location	Spp	Adult Male	Adult Female	Yearlings Male	Yearlings Female	Calf/ Kid	Unclassified	Remarks
7·49	1	SIKA		1					
8·10	2	"		1					
8·34	3	"	1						Visibility improving 09·00
9·10	4	"	1	1					Stag laying down
9·15	5	"	2						
9·20	6	"		4	Groups	5 & 6	came	together & fed	up burnside
9·36	Male 3	seen	again	feeding					
9·54	7	"		1					
10·03	Group 4	now	on feet	feeding					
10·05	8			1	very	pregnant			
10·27	9							1	Deer No 2 also up & feeding
10·35	10								
			5	8				1	= 14/47 ha
									≡ 29·8/100 ha

Figure 3.6 *Vantage point count record form for density estimation of woodland deer in hilly terrain*

26

5. Aerial counts

Method

Where deer are resident on open ground, or mainly open habitat, it may be possible to observe them readily from the air using either a light aircraft, microlight or helicopter. The observer(s) counts animals seen as the aircraft flies predetermined transects over the area. The width of the piece of ground viewed depends upon the height at which the aircraft is travelling and how far from the aircraft the observer(s) can see (delimited by fitting streamers to the wing struts). Therefore any change in flight height needs to be corrected for in the calculations. The use of thermal imaging equipment and videos or photography to record images detected (for later checking) is advised as this enables double counting to be eliminated. The method is described in detail by Sutherland (1996) and Norton-Griffiths (1978). Detection of animals from the air is better following snow cover as they show up more clearly both thermally and visually. The method is most suitable for large deer populations, and is not recommended where the area and population are small.

Data recorded   Species, sex- and age-class, and direction of travel of all animals seen.

Equipment required   Aircraft and pilot, map of area with transects clearly marked, 1-2 observers, photographic/video equipment or thermal imaging equipment.

H & S considerations   Flying may be dangerous in some terrains particularly where weather is unpredictable.

Advantages
- Large areas of deer range can be covered in a relatively short period of time.
- It is possible to view down into open woodland habitats, particularly when using a microlight, without disturbing the deer.
- Estimate of minimum population size is likely to be better than for visual methods from the ground.
- Species composition, sex- and age-class ratios can be determined if deer can be seen sufficiently clearly.
- Only 2–4 people required.

Disadvantages
- Most suited to flat or rolling terrain (see above).
- Requires good visibility and flying conditions.
- Accuracy influenced by height of aircraft above the ground, and tendency of deer to bunch and run off wildly, making assessment of numbers, age- and sex-classes difficult. (Microlights cause less disturbance.)
- Accuracy may be influenced by the presence of other animals, e.g. sheep (see Example below).
- Results specific to day of count and liable to influences of seasonal changes in climate and deer behaviour.
- Hire of aircraft may be expensive and operation requires much planning.

Performance as an estimate	****
Performance as an index	*****
Inexpensive equipment costs	*
Inexpensive labour costs	****
Simple data analysis	***
Data collection period	1–2 days

Example

The Deer Commission for Scotland, in collaboration with Scottish Natural Heritage, investigated the use of helicopter mounted thermal imaging equipment for aerial surveys at two sites during 1993 (Reynolds *et al.*, 1994) and found close agreement between total count numbers for this and traditional open hill counts (see 1) in the study areas. At the first site, 137 deer were seen from the air while 136 were counted on the ground. At the second site, 2 observers counted 428 and 452 deer from the air while the ground count was 404. The discrepancy was believed to be due to sheep being misclassified as deer in the thermal imaging results.

Night counts

Deer tend to move out onto open areas to feed at night and are often more easily approached, particularly when the observer is in a vehicle. Night vision equipment can be used to observe and count deer in areas where daytime observation is not possible. Low cost night vision equipment, such as spotlights and image intensifiers, have a limited application as their shorter detection distances will tend to lead to more disturbance to the deer, which will influence the population estimate.

Thermal imaging

Thermal imaging equipment (Plate 2) is sensitive to the long-wave radiant energy emitted by warm-bodied animals and their surrounding habitat, revealing surface temperature differences with varying brightness on a viewfinder or video screen (Plate 3). Modern thermal imagers are sensitive to very small temperature differences (<0.1°C), making deer particularly conspicuous even if partly concealed. In the open, deer may be visible at distances of up to 2 km, with species and sex differences becoming increasingly discernible at closer range.

Thermal imaging equipment can be used hand held from the ground or a vehicle, or may be mounted on an aircraft. Since foliage will conceal many deer, aircraft mounted systems are more suited to open areas or woodland with a sparse canopy. An imager used from the ground provides a lateral view giving relatively better penetration into most stand types.

To date, imagers originally designed for weapons targeting applications have been found to be best suited for deer density estimation (see Appendix 5 for suppliers). These are portable and provide good image resolution and magnification. Less expensive night vision equipment, including low-cost thermal imagers, spotlights or image intensifiers, are less likely to reveal partly concealed deer, reducing the number of detections and increasing the risk of disturbing animals prior to detection. Such equipment is not recommended.

In view of the fact that thermal energy will not penetrate foliage, an estimating technique such as distance sampling (8) is the most appropriate method to use in woodland. However direct counts can be used in the following situations:

- When surveying open areas (fields, parks or moorland).
- When a large proportion of the population emerges from woodland to use nearby open ground at night.

This arises in some red, fallow and occasionally roe deer populations. A decision to base an estimate on counts in this instance should only be made if the woodland has been extensively surveyed and a large proportion of the deer (>75%) was observed outside the wood.

In practice, most areas to be surveyed include a proportion of woodland and open ground and population size is best estimated using a *combination* of both distance sampling and direct count methods.

6. Spotlight counts

Method

Deer moving out onto open areas at night can be counted, with care, with the aid of spotlights, which pick out the eyes of any animals (up to 300 m away) facing the observer. Deer passing close to the observer (up to 50 m) may be seen sufficiently clearly to sex or age them. Usually the area to be counted is identified and visited at night with one person driving the vehicle (on sidelights to reduce disturbance), another operating the spotlight (either roof mounted or handheld) and a third recording all observations. If a sampling method (such as distance sampling) is used then population density and confidence limits may be determined. However, the method is only suitable in areas where deer are undisturbed at night, as they will flee rapidly at the sound of a vehicle or glimpse of a light in areas where night shooting (legal or otherwise) occurs. This method is limited in use and therefore not recommended.

Data recorded　Where possible, species, sex- and age-class of all animals seen. Perpendicular distance to observed deer (if distance sampling).

Equipment required　Spotlight, vehicle with roof hatch or open back, 1–3 observers/assistants, map of the area and record forms.

H & S considerations　Risks associated with driving at night with sidelights only (to reduce disturbance). Risks can be reduced by reconnoitre of the route during daylight to identify hazards such as low branches and potholes.

Advantages
- Relatively quick method.
- Low labour requirement (2–4 people).
- Low cost equipment.

Disadvantages
- Only suitable in areas with a good system of rides, roads or tracks.
- Requires good visibility.
- Only minimum population size can be estimated and accuracy probably poor.
- Difficult to determine age- and sex-class.
- In areas where night shooting occurs deer may respond by fleeing rapidly at the sound of a vehicle.
- Results specific to day of count and liable to influences of seasonal changes in climate and deer behaviour.

Performance as an estimate	**
Performance as an index	***
Inexpensive equipment costs	***
Inexpensive labour costs	****
Simple data analysis	***
Data collection period	1–7 days

Example

Spotlighting was used in a lowland broadleaved woodland as a means of estimating kid:doe ratios during September–October 1979 and January–March 1980 (Rowe, unpublished). During both periods too few individuals were seen to provide good estimates of kid:doe ratios, in part due to the fact that 30% of all deer seen could not be classified as male, female or kid, and it was not possible to distinguish between adult and yearling females. No attempt was made to determine population size based on these observations.

7. Thermal imaging: direct counts

Counts may be made from a number of locations through or around the survey areas. Sites should be chosen that offer the most extensive view, bearing in mind the range of the imager and any hedges, hollows or convex slopes that may conceal deer. At each location, it is important to mark on a 1 : 10 000 map the area visible.

If the total area to be surveyed is relatively small and all locations can be assessed with little risk of deer moving between them, then the estimated population size is simply the sum of all deer counted. If however there is the possibility of movement between areas, then population size should be estimated from the mean density of deer seen on each area multiplied by the total area. It is advisable to repeat the exercise on subsequent nights, and take the mean of each night's estimate. It is important to try to eliminate observer disturbance when moving between areas.

Data recorded Number, species, sex- and age-class of all animals seen.

Equipment required A high resolution thermal imager. For vehicle censuses a 4-wheel drive vehicle with a roof hatch is recommended. A compass with a luminous dial is needed to take bearings.

H&S considerations Particular care should be taken when walking through woodlands at night while viewing through the thermal imager. Routes on steep or unstable ground should be avoided by vehicles. All routes should be checked for hazards in daylight immediately prior to sampling.

Advantages
- Accuracy high.
- Species composition can be estimated.
- Sex- and age-classes can be estimated if males in velvet.
- Group sizes can be estimated.
- Nocturnal behaviour can be observed.
- Camouflaged animals easily detected.
- Open areas can often be viewed from public highways.

Disadvantages
- Not suitable within woodland.
- The availability of thermal imaging equipment is currently limited and costs are very high: up to £40K (see Appendix 5 for suppliers).
- Usually limited to small woods or areas with little woodland cover.
- Results specific to count days and liable to influences of seasonal changes in climate and deer behaviour, unless total deer home range is sampled.
- Distinguishing between similar species and shapes (sheep and deer) can be difficult.

Performance as an estimate	*****
Performance as an index	*****
Inexpensive equipment costs	**
Inexpensive labour costs	****
Simple data analysis	*****
Data collection period	1–3 days

8. Thermal imaging: distance sampling

Method

The estimation of population density using distance sampling relies on the calculation of a *detection function* from the distances measured between groups of deer and the transect line. The detection function defines the probability of detecting deer at a given distance from the transect, and makes it possible to estimate density from the number of deer encountered along the route sampled. In view of the fact that visibility depends on vegetation density, it may be necessary to treat any large contiguous areas that differ in vegetation structure as separate strata (see Stratified sampling in Section 2), and calculate a detection function for each. However, it is usually only necessary to separate forest areas from any open ground immediately adjacent to the forest.

It is important to ensure that the extent of possible diurnal and seasonal movements are considered when planning a survey. Transect routes surveyed on any one night should encompass areas known or likely to be used both day and night by the deer, to avoid the risk of over- or under-detection.

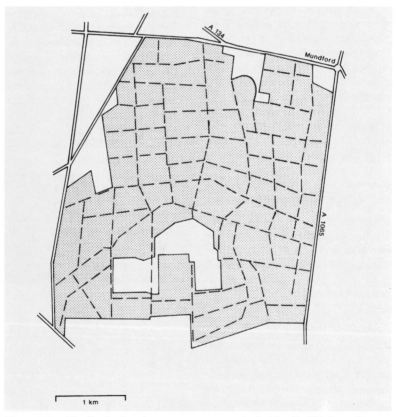

Figure 3.7 *The distribution of transect routes to sample the Mundford block. -- Forest rides/roads used as transect routes; these should be well distributed across the survey area*

32

It will be acceptable to survey only summer or winter ground if it is safe to assume there are no deer remaining on the unsurveyed habitats at that particular time of year. If not, it will be necessary to survey both summer and winter habitats.

The deer population range and area to be surveyed should be clearly identified on a map on which the transect lines should be marked (Figure 3.7). For practical reasons transects should follow existing forest roads and paths. It is important that the routes surveyed are representative of the forest as a whole, i.e. that they pass through the range of stand types that occur in the survey area.

Sampling intensity needs to be high enough to ensure that areas of high density are not over- or under-represented in the sample. To achieve this the minimum ratio of ride/road length sampled (in km) to forest area (in km^2) should be at least 2.5 although more is preferable. Roads/rides should penetrate all areas of the forest, with no area >~300 m wide or >~10 ha unpenetrated. This effectively ensures that about 30% or more of the woodland area is sampled. The density of roads/rides sampled can be reduced in larger forest blocks (~2000 ha) provided routes are well distributed throughout the area. In this event, precision is likely to be improved by subdividing the area into strata and sampling each area separately. Transect routes may be any length (300–2000 m is ideal) and should start and end at the forest edge or at road/ride intersections. The use of two or more routes in close proximity should be avoided on the same night, to avoid the risk of disturbing deer from a previous route. There should be 10–25 transect routes within each woodland (precision will tend to increase with the number of transects sampled). All routes should be marked and clearly identified on a 1 : 10 000 map of the area.

Transects should be followed either on foot (walking into wind and without using a torch) or using a vehicle (using only sidelights and at 5–15 kph), taking care to minimise disturbance. Vegetation either side of the transect should be scanned for the presence of deer. When passing dense vegetation vehicle speed should be kept to 5 kph and scans repeated approximately every 5 seconds. Where the route passes large patches of dense vegetation it is usually easier to focus on one side of the vehicle, and return to the other side of this part of the route on another night. In this situation the part of the route sampled in such a way is considered as half the length. Scanning from back–front gives more uniform coverage than from front–back.

Table 3.3a *Average body length of each species/sex used to estimate distance (cm)*

Species	Males	Females	Unsexed	Juvenile
Fallow	135	125	130	105
Muntjac	80	80	80	65
Roe deer	100	100	100	80
Red deer	170	150	160	120
Sika deer	140	125	132	105

For each group of deer observed, the perpendicular distance from the transect line should be estimated and the number of deer counted and classified by species, sex and age, where possible. Distances should be estimated *before* the deer move away, or if they have already moved, the distance to their position before they took flight should be estimated. If the group is scattered, the distance to an animal close to the group centre should be estimated. Distances should be measured by one of the following two methods.

Rangefinder
Measure length of body, nose–rump, standing side on, against rangefinding marks (Figure 3.8 and Table 3.3a). This should be measured before the group moves

away in reaction to the observer and preferably on an animal at the centre of the group. If a side-on view proves impossible then use the map method described below or measure the width across ear tips and assume that this is a proportion of body length (see Table 3.3b).

Table 3.3b *Width across ears as a proportion of nose–tail length (%). Ear width measured when facing either directly towards or away from observer*

Species	%
Fallow	30
Muntjac	29
Roe deer	25
Red deer	28
Sika deer	27

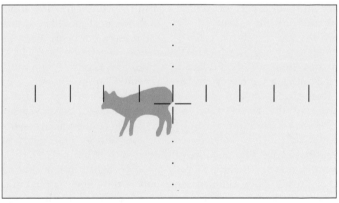

Distances can be estimated if thermal imager is equipped with an internal rangefinder:

$$\text{Distance (m)} = k \times \frac{\text{Object length (m)}}{\text{Length in viewfinder}}$$

The value of k depends on the type of imager and lens being used and is calculated from the angle between rangefinding marks (θ):

$$k = \left[\frac{2 \tan \left(\frac{\theta}{2} \right)}{2} \right]^{-1}$$

In this example, using a Pilkington lite imager with a x9 lens ($\theta = 0.57°$) and assuming body length is 1.00 m for an adult roe deer, the distance is:

$$100.5 \times \frac{1.00}{2.1} = 48 \text{ m}$$

Figure 3.8 *Distance estimate through rangefinder*

34

Detection distance (y_d) is calculated from average body length (Table 3.3a), body length as measured through the rangefinder, and the angle through the rangefinding marks.

The compass bearing° of the group from the observer (ϕ_1) and the bearing° of the direction of the route (ϕ_2) from where the observation was made must also be recorded. The perpendicular distance is then equal to $\sin(\phi_1-\phi_2)y_d$ (Figure 3.9). A computer program for converting body lengths and angles into perpendicular distances is available from the authors.

Map

Mark the position of the group and the observer on a 1:10 000 map as accurately as possible. Perpendicular distance can be measured from the map afterwards. Where the road bends, the shortest perpendicular distance should be taken (see Figure 3.10). This method is preferable if the group is distant (>200 m), the route bends or body length cannot be measured.

Species may be identified from body proportions (leg:body length), alarm call, group size, antler shape and gait, particularly when taking flight.

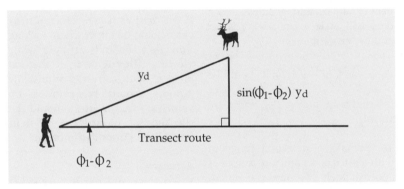

Figure 3.9 *Calculation of the perpendicular distance from a deer to the transect line*

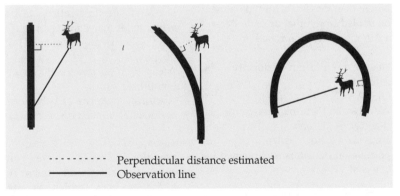

- - - - - - - - - Perpendicular distance estimated
——————— Observation line

Figure 3.10 *Measurement of the perpendicular distance of observed deer from a transect route when plotting deer on a map: three typical scenarios*

It is more difficult to identify species as observation distance increases, particularly >500 m. Sex can only usually be distinguished reliably when males are in velvet. Closer approach usually aids identification, but should only be attempted after the distance from the group has been estimated.

Each road/ride should be surveyed 1–3 times, on different nights, preferably covering the same length each time. The length surveyed should be measured from the map (to the nearest 100 m) and recorded on the census form (see Appendix 4). Transects should not be sampled in bad weather (storms, high winds, heavy rain or falling snow) when deer will make more use of cover and be less visible.

For an area of ~1000 ha it should be possible to carry out a census over 5–8 nights by foot or 2–3 nights by vehicle.

To estimate a 'detection function' with sufficient accuracy, a sample of approximately 50 groups is required. However 70 is recommended. Where insufficient observations are obtained (in small woodlands or where deer density is low) data may be pooled from other areas to derive a common detection function.

Deer population density is estimated using the program DISTANCE (available on the Worldwide Web http://www.ruwpa. st-and.ac.uk/distance/). The data analysis and calculation of population densities is explained in Gill *et al.* (1997).

Data recorded   Number, species, sex- and age-class of all animals in a group, and distance of the group from the transect line.

Equipment required   For woodland censuses, a high resolution thermal imager with built in rangefinder (for distance sampling). (In daylight an optical or laser rangefinder may be used.) For vehicle censuses a 4 wheel drive vehicle with a roof hatch is recommended. A compass with a luminous dial is needed to take bearings, and two-way radios for driver–observer communications are also recommended.

H & S considerations   Particular care should be taken when walking through woodlands at night while viewing through the thermal imager. Routes on steep or unstable ground should be avoided by vehicles. All routes should be checked for hazards in daylight immediately prior to sampling.

Advantages
- Accuracy and reliability good if assumptions valid.
- Species composition can be estimated.
- Sex- and age-class ratios can be estimated if males in velvet.
- Low labour requirement (1–2 people).
- Areas of high deer use can be identified.
- Nocturnal patterns of behaviour and habitat use can be observed.

Disadvantages
- Woodland must have an extensive ride/road network ≥2.5 km km^{-2}, which is not associated with deer habitat use.
- Requires the use of specialist computer software to analyse

data and calculate population density.

- Results specific to count days and liable to influences of seasonal changes in climate and deer behaviour.
- Training in the use of equipment, sampling method and analysis are recommended.
- The availability of thermal imaging equipment is currently limited and performance and prices (£7000–£40 000) of equipment are variable (see Appendix 5).
- Bias may occur where deer are avoiding or attracted to roads/rides. This is detectable in the data analysis.

Performance as an estimate	*****
Performance as an index	*****
Inexpensive equipment costs	**
Inexpensive labour costs	****
Simple data analysis	*
Data collection period	3–5 days

Example

Thermal imaging was used to estimate the size of the deer (red, roe and muntjac) population in the Mundford block (~1200 ha), Thetford Forest during April/May 1996. Transects within the woodland block followed forest roads, tracks or firebreaks (Figure 3.7). Twenty-nine transects totalling 61.6 km were sampled. The use of transects in close proximity (<500 m) on the same night was minimised to reduce the risk of detecting deer disturbed from a previous route. Routes were travelled two or three times if necessary, until sufficient data had been obtained (>50 observed groups) to calculate a population density. As deer also used fields adjacent to the woodland block these areas were surveyed and the results added to the estimate obtained from distance sampling.

All observed groups of deer were classified by species, sex- and age-class; group size and distance from the observer were estimated. The data were analysed using the procedures outlined by Buckland *et al.* (1993), using their software 'DISTANCE'.

The overall population estimate for the Mundford block was 23.2 km^{-2} (95% confidence interval 17.9 – 30.0 km^{-2}).

Other direct methods

The following methods can be used to estimate population densities, or to provide an index of population size. However, they are of limited use to practical deer managers due to the resources required to achieve sufficiently large sample sizes or the low accuracy levels achieved.

9. Individual recognition (mark–resighting)

Method

In populations where it is possible to individually recognise a sufficiently large number of the population (from either natural markings or capture–marking programmes) the population size can be estimated from the proportion of recognisable individuals in the observed sample. In most deer species it is difficult to observe and recognise individuals unless many hours are spent observing the population (particularly in woodlands), and so animals require capture and marking for this method. Care must be taken that marking effort is distributed equally across the whole survey area, and that it does not introduce bias, by altering behaviour patterns or mortality levels. If the population is totally enclosed, or it can be assumed that there are no gains (births or immigration) or losses (deaths or emigration) during the period between marking and resighting then the population is assumed to be '*closed*'. For most wild deer populations these assumptions are not valid and so the population is considered to be '*open*'.

Various models to analyse mark–recapture data and estimate population size are available (Greenwood, 1996). Although applicable to both open and closed populations open population models produce less precise estimates of population size as they make fewer assumptions. However, although more precise, if closed population models are applied to open populations they will provide biased estimates (generally higher). However if the period between capture and resighting is sufficiently short and at a time when it is reasonable to assume that there has been no loss or gain of animals to the population from emigration, immigration, births or deaths then closed population models can be used. The use of radio-telemetry will also assist in determining the number of marked animals in an open population.

Where one cannot be sure about whether the population is open or closed it is better to use an open model as an imprecise but unbiased estimate is generally preferred to a precise but biased estimate. The Jolly–Seber model is most suitable for analysing open deer populations, but tends to produce imprecise density estimates unless a high proportion of the population is marked (Strandgaard, 1972). Capture–resighting techniques are therefore most suitable for research projects, due to the effort and costs involved with observing and/ or marking individual deer. Additionally a licence to capture and mark deer is required from the statutory conservation bodies.

Data recorded Individual deer identity (number/mark), dates seen, total number of deer seen on each occasion.

Equipment required If marking deer, clearly coloured collars and ear tags; equipment and licence to catch and handle the animals.

H & S considerations Risks of injury to staff and deer during catching operations. Additional risks associated with chemical immobilisation.

Advantages
- Precision can be estimated.
- Sex- and age-class ratios can be estimated.

Disadvantages
- Precision dependent upon validity of assumptions, and liable to bias if assumptions not valid for the model used.
- High labour (observation time and deer capture) and catching and marking equipment costs.
- Licence required to catch and mark adult deer.
- Careful, detailed organisation required and staff skilled in catching and handling deer.
- Complex software required for data analysis.

Performance as an estimate	****
Performance as an index	****
Inexpensive equipment costs	*
Inexpensive labour costs	*
Simple data analysis	**

Data collection period	3–24 months

Example

Gill *et al.* (1996) estimated population size for a marked roe deer population at Chedington Wood, Dorset. They used the joint hypergeometric maximum likelihood estimator (White and Garrott, 1990) which is suited to observation data rather than recapture data. Deer were caught and released onto the study area each March. Repeat censuses shortly after release were then used (up to 36 per year) to estimate the ratio of marked : unmarked deer on each day.

Counts from each census day were pooled and population size estimated as follows:

Estimated population size =

$$\frac{\text{Number of marked deer alive} \times \left[\frac{\text{Sum of total deer seen in}}{\text{all censuses}} +1\right]}{\left[\text{Sum of marked deer seen in all censuses} +1\right]}$$

For example:
Total number of deer marked = 80

	Censuses			
	April	May	June	Sum
Total deer seen	100	79	120	299
Marked deer seen	30	40	29	99

Estimated population size $\dfrac{80 \times 300}{100}$ = 240 deer

The method assumes that the population is 'closed', that loss of marks is accounted for, all animals have the same probability of being caught and resighted, and that each census is independent.

At Chedington Wood the population size varied from 46 km^{-2} in spring 1967 to 76 km^{-2} in 1975, falling again to 34 km^{-2} in 1979/80; 95% confidence intervals varied from ± 0 to 12. In most years the percentage marked (of the minimum number alive) in each spring was >78%. The lowest proportion of marked animals in any year was estimated to be 64% in 1966 while the maximum was 89% in 1976.

10. Change-in-ratio counts

By observing and recording sex, age-class or marked–unmarked ratios, just prior to and following a known cull, it is possible to calculate a population estimate before the cull based on the change in ratios and known mortality.

The method assumes the population is 'closed' (i.e. that there are no gains/losses unaccounted for during the period between surveys). This is valid if the range of a population is well defined and the cull period between surveys is short.

Method

The sex ratio of the population is estimated from observations directly before and after the male cull and before the female cull (e.g. at the beginning of July and early October for red deer stags). The population size before the cull can be estimated from the observed sex ratios and known cull between the survey dates using this equation:

$$\hat{N}_1 = \frac{R_s - R \times P_2}{P_1 - P_2}$$

where

$\hat{N}_1$ = Estimated population size before the cull.

R_s = Number of stags removed between surveys 1 and 2.

R = Total number of stags and hinds removed between survey 1 and 2.

P_1 = Proportion of stags before the cull.

P_2 = Proportion of stags after the cull.

Population size before the hind cull can be estimated using the same equation (replacing 'stags' with 'hinds' in all cases) and data gathered before and after the hind cull.

The method assumes males and females are seen with equal probability, which may not be valid where there are behavioural and range use differences between sexes. Sample sizes need to be large to be confident of the accuracy of the ratios calculated, particularly where the change in ratio before and after the cull is small. Where the population is not 'closed' (i.e. there are losses from poaching and natural mortality), the assumptions are not valid and the population size will be underestimated. Conner *et al.* (1986) discuss sample sizes and calculation of variance estimates to determine accuracy.

If there are problems in accurately classifying individuals to sex then another feature such as with/without antlers can be used. Buckland (1992) proposed this method as a means of checking bias in open hill red deer counts (1) and suggested that it may be particularly useful for checking on estimates of open hill red deer populations which have access to forestry blocks and therefore an unknown proportion of the population may be hidden at any given time.

Data recorded   Number of animals by species, sex- and age-class.

Equipment required   Binoculars, telescopes.

H & S considerations   Risks associated with lone working: minimise risks by set daily reporting procedures and provision of mobile phones.

Advantages
- Suitable for large areas.
- Sex- and age-class ratios can be estimated.
- Provides a check on open hill count bias.
- Low equipment costs.

Disadvantages
- Large sample of observations required (most suited to open habitat).
- Good visibility required.
- Precision influenced by observer bias in sex and age classification.
- Precision influenced by seasonal changes in deer behaviour.
- Two separate surveys required.

Performance as an estimate	***
Performance as an index	****
Inexpensive equipment costs	***
Inexpensive labour costs	***
Simple data analysis	***
Data collection period	6–9 months

Example

Changes in sex ratio pre- and post-culling were used to estimate the size of a woodland roe deer population before the doe cull. On a day during early October, 20 observers were positioned for 3 hours around the outside of the woodland block to observe deer coming out onto fields to feed. Another two observers were inside the wood. A total of 187 individual deer were seen in ratios of 1 adult male : 3 adult females (0.25:0.75). The overall ratio (including kids) was 1 male : 2 females (0.33:0.67).

During the doe cull, 53 adults and 21 kids were removed. On the second observation at the end of March, 288 deer were seen; the ratio

of adult males to adult females was 1:2 (0.33:0.67) and the overall ratio (including kids) was 1 male : 1.8 females (0.36:0.64).

The population (N) at the time of the first observation was estimated from

$$N = \frac{R_D - R \times P_2}{P_1 - P_2}$$

where

R_D = Number of does culled.

Based on the overall sex ratio counts (adults + kids),

$$N = \frac{74 - (74 \times 0.64)}{0.67 - 0.64} = 888$$

Based on adult only sex ratios,

$$N = \frac{53 - (53 \times 0.67)}{0.75 - 0.67} = 219.$$

The widely differing results indicate the problems associated with this method due to seasonal deer behaviour and possible misclassification. During October, it is possible some animals were living out on the fields and had not moved back to the woodland. The proportion of bucks seen during the first observation may have been reduced due to seasonal behaviour, and there may have been bias in age estimation during the second observation, with well-grown kids counted as adults. Care was taken to ensure no double counting occurred; however, it is possible that this may have led to an underestimate in the number of deer actually observed, as animals assumed to have been seen twice on the same day may actually have been separate individuals.

Table 3.4 *Index of deer presence from browsing and grazing impacts (after Mitchell and Kirby, 1990)*

Trees and shrubs	No regeneration due to competition from dense ground vegetation.	Creation of regeneration niches.	Loss of seedlings. Damage to saplings.	Loss of saplings. Severe tree browsing.	Barking of mature trees. Loss of shrub layer.	Creation of parkland or moorland.
Field layer plants	Reduced diversity dominated by a few vigorous species.	Reduction in vigorous species. Increase in species diversity.	Reduction in vegetation structure. Increase in grazing tolerant species.	Loss of plant diversity, particularly of grazing sensitive species.	Loss of cover and damage due to trampling. Bare ground.	Impoverishment due to net loss of nutrients from the system.
Ground layer plants	Reduced cover and diversity due to competition from field layer plants.	Increase in cover of ground layer species as competition from field layer plants reduced.		Damage to ground layer species due to trampling.	Reduction of drought sensitive bryophytes.	Increase in epiphytic lichens associated with parkland.

No grazing → High and sustained grazing intensity

Deer presence   Low   Medium   High

Optimum grazing intensity

42

Indirect methods of measuring deer populations

Where deer use woodland or other concealing habitats for a part or most of the time, direct methods of population estimation are likely to be inaccurate. Ratcliffe (1987) and Langbein (1996) suggest population underestimates of a factor of 4. Indirect methods of determining population size and density should be considered. Signs such as tracks/slots (Plate 4), fraying and browsing, scrapes and faecal pellet groups have been investigated (Dzieciolowski, 1976), with varying levels of success. Usually the area is sampled to determine a mean level of sign presence and this is then related to previous information on deer density, presence and decay of the sign in other known populations. If the presence of the sign is not expected to be similar across the whole site, stratification (see Stratified sampling) will be required before sampling begins.

Scrapes and fraying stocks. Scrapes and fraying stocks tend to be associated with territorial marking and may be more frequent where competition for access to females is greatest (e.g. where there is a high male : female ratio) or in open areas. Therefore they will not be dispersed evenly throughout an area. Additionally, there are no background data indicating the number of scrapes or fraying stocks associated with an individual territory. They are therefore not a practical method of assessing deer densities and population size, but are useful in indicating where territorial males may be resident.

11. Impact levels

Browsing and grazing impact levels may be used to provide an index of deer presence: high, medium, low (Table 3.4, opposite). Impact levels on a site will be influenced by the number of deer present and their feeding behaviour, habitat type, and the availability (presence and whether protected or not) of preferred and vulnerable plant species. For these reasons no simple relationship has been found between deer numbers and impact levels. There does, however, appear to be a threshold density for any habitat, below which very little damage seems to occur, and above which damage/impact will be noticeable (Gill, 1992). This threshold density will also depend upon land management objectives. In many situations unacceptable impact levels (to the crop/habitat) will be the reason for deciding to estimate deer population size.

Method

Impact levels can be measured by determining browsing /grazing levels in sample plots taken across the whole deer range or within various habitat strata, depending upon the detail required and resources available. Tree crop impact levels (% trees damaged) can be determined using the 'nearest neighbour' technique (Pepper, 1998). Other vegetation may be assessed for the proportion grazed/browsed, or % cover (e.g. by species, groups), and a score allocated to each factor which can then be totalled to provide an index of overall deer impact. Ferris-Kaan and Patterson (1992) describe methods for monitoring vegetation, and sampling design and layout are discussed in Sampling in Section 2. The number and size of samples taken will depend upon the methods to be used and resources available. Generally, samples should be allocated at random within each habitat stratum.

Data recorded   Deer species present, type of tree protection (if any), proportion of damaged trees, impact scores for other vegetation.

Equipment required   Record forms, quadrats for vegetation assessments.

H & S considerations   Risks associated with lone working: minimise risks by set daily reporting procedures and provision of mobile phones.

Advantages
• Applicable in all habitats.
• Low labour requirement (1-2 people).
• Low equipment costs.

Disadvantages
• Imprecise.
• Only an 'index' of deer presence can be established.
• Seasonal deer behaviour and impacts will cause bias and influence choice of sampling date.
• Impacts from sheep, rabbits, hares, etc. may be difficult to separate from deer impacts.

Performance as an estimate	*
Performance as an index	***
Inexpensive equipment costs	***
Inexpensive labour costs	***
Simple data analysis	***

Data collection period	1–5 days crop 6-12 months habitat

Example

In a study of farm woodland damage, the proportion of trees damaged by deer or rabbit was recorded separately for each woodland visited (Mayle, unpublished). Protection used on the trees varied between woodlands and within woodlands with some woods having individual tree protection of different heights and design for the various tree/shrub species planted. Deer browsing levels varied from 0% in woodlands where treeshelters of adequate height (1.8 m for fallow deer) were used to 84% where trees had not been protected against deer browsing.

12. Track/slot counts

In areas where there is reliable snow cover, deer tracks or 'slots' have been used as a means of estimating relative deer densities by comparing the number of tracks entering with the number leaving an area on the next day (Dzieciolowski, 1976). This assumes that an animal passes through the same place on consecutive days. However, as this assumption is not necessarily true, the method is best used to provide an index of deer activity rather than numbers (Pucek *et al.*, 1975). The method has also been tried in areas where soil type (sandy/loam) enables clear imprints or slots (Plate 4) to be formed, by either counting the number of regularly used pathways crossing the woodland boundary (Plate 5) or the number of slots formed in prepared ground over a specified period of time.

Method

Deer pathways crossing woodland boundaries are best counted during spring/early summer when ground vegetation is not too dense and pathways can be more easily seen. The observer walks around the outside of the woodland block and records the number of deer pathways crossing the boundary for each 100m (paces). Fencing around the woodland boundary may restrict deer access and hence the number of pathways. The average number of pathways per 100 m is then used as an index of deer presence.

Data recorded   Number of pathways crossing the woodlands boundary per 100 m.

H & S considerations   Risks associated with lone working: minimise risks by set daily reporting procedures and provision of mobile phones.

Advantages

- Suitable in most habitats.
- Relatively quick.
- Low labour requirement.
- Low equipment costs.

Disadvantages

- Dense, grassy vegetation may obscure pathways.
- Only of use to provide an index of presence or activity.
- No sex or age classification possible.
- Unreliable as an estimate as main assumption often not valid.

Performance as an estimate	*
Performance as an index	***
Inexpensive equipment costs	*****
Inexpensive labour costs	*****
Simple data analysis	****
Data collection period	1-4 days

Example

Mayle *et al.* (in prep.) found correlations between faecal pellet group counts and trackway counts per 100 m in sites with mainly fallow and roe deer present. Faecal pellet decay was assumed to be 6 months across all sites and for both species, providing density indices of 1 to 10 km^{-2} for roe and 1 to 22 km^{-2} for fallow deer. The number of trackways per 100 m tended to be 4 times greater for roe than for fallow at the same deer density index; i.e. at 10 deer km^{-2} there were approximately 8 pathways for roe but only 2 for fallow deer sites.

Faecal pellet counts

Faecal pellet groups are one of the most obvious signs that deer are present in an area. They are found in all habitat types and can be used either to provide an index of deer presence or an estimate of population density in different habitats from which total population size across the deer range can be calculated. Faecal pellet group counts are best carried out in spring and autumn. A faecal pellet group is defined as a cluster of 6 or more pellets produced at the same defecation.

Two groups lying close together or one on top of the other can usually be distinguished by differences in colour, size and texture. Groups found on the edge of a transect or plot should be counted or rejected based on the number of pellets in the group lying inside or outside the search area. When groups lie exactly on the edge they should be alternately included and rejected. Occasionally individual pellets are seen but these are often part of a group which has been defecated while the animal has been moving, causing them to be scattered in a line or string ('stringers'). Such individual pellets should be noted and care taken when searching to follow the line of these pellets across the boundaries of the transect or section of the plot being searched.

Prior to fieldwork it is advisable to check that staff involved use the same search technique, and are equally competent at identifying faecal pellet groups to species where more than one species of ungulate is present (Appendix 6). It will probably not be possible to identify all groups to species and so 'possible roe/muntjac' etc. categories will also need to be recorded.

Estimate of population density and size

Faecal pellet group counts to estimate deer population density fall into two main categories: *faecal accumulation rates (FAR)* or clearance counts and *faecal standing crop counts (FSC)*. The choice of method will depend on the level of accuracy required, the time available, how soon the result is required, and the density of deer in the area. Clearance counts (involving two site visits) tend to be more accurate as variation due to pellet group decay will be either reduced to a minimum or eliminated. The latter will occur where plots are revisited before fresh pellet groups marked during the first visit have disappeared. Clearance counts are most practical at high deer densities (above 30 km^{-2}).

At lower deer densities, standing crop counts are most practical in terms of effort and accuracy. Three sampling regimes can be used: plots, as for clearance counts; transects; and line transects. Before standing crop counts are carried out decay should be monitored in each of the habitats to be sampled, and for each of the deer species being considered (see Appendix 7). Where a site is visited regularly (monthly) decay monitoring can be included during the visit, otherwise separate visits may be required.

Both methods use information on faecal pellet group decay (Appendix 7) and defecation rate (Appendix 8) along with the faecal pellet group count results to estimate population density, and so the overall accuracy of the population estimate will be influenced by the accuracy associated with the estimate of defecation and decay rates, as well as by the sampling regime. Although they may be carried out at any time of the year, faecal pellet counts are best done during late winter/early spring, after snow has melted and before vegetation growth starts.

Sampling regimes will vary depending upon the approach to be used and the resources available. For all methods it is recommended that all habitats (woodland and open) used by the deer population are sampled and that the total deer range is first stratified (see Stratified sampling in Section 2) to increase the precision of the final population estimate. As faecal pellet group decay will also vary between habitats, stratification should also consider variation in pellet group decay.

The number of sample plots required depends upon the precision required and resources available. When using faecal pellet group counts, deer population size is usually estimated to ±20%. To achieve this, at least 100 faecal pellet groups need to be counted in total. If the precision required is ±10%, then the sample size should be increased so that at least 400 pellet groups are counted in total. The number of plots required to ensure 100 pellet groups are counted depends upon the expected mean

number of pellet groups per plot; this is influenced by deer density, daily defecation rate and decay time for the pellet groups. A pilot study or previous information may be used to indicate expected mean number of pellet groups per plot. Table 3.5 provides examples of the minimum number of plots required to achieve ±20% precision for varying deer densities and decay lengths based on results of previous faecal pellet group count studies.

Where the area to be counted has been stratified, plots should be allocated proportionally (page 11) to each habitat with a minimum number of 6 plots in each habitat type. Plots should ideally be allocated to representatives of each stratum at random as in the following example.

Example of plot allocation

Habitat 1 (total area: 550 ha) is represented by 15 blocks (a-o) with individual areas as listed in Table 3.6. The running total for the habitat area is listed beside the plots and used with the random number table (Appendix 1) to determine within which block the samples should be taken. As the total area is 550 ha, we can use the 3 digit groups within the table. Suppose the 13th

Table 3.5 *Number of 7m x 7m plots required to achieve ±20% accuracy for standing crop counts*

Density (km^{-2})	Decay length (months)	Mean pellet groups per plot	Minimum number of plots to sample[a]
<10	9	1.8	55
10-20	4-6	1.3	77
40-50	3	6.9	15
20-27	3-4	3	35

[a] Minimum of 6 plots per habitat stratum.

row in the table is randomly selected. The numbers are 797, 844, 747, 041, 433, 658, 062, 922, 410, 107, 154, 252, 679, 874, 785, 468, 084, 348. As the total area is only 550 ha, the first three numbers are ignored; the fourth number, 041, identifies the block in which the first plot is placed – block C (running total 45); 433 identifies the block in which the second plot is placed – block N (running total 460), and so on giving the sample plot allocation shown in Table 3.6. Within each block, plots should be randomly sited using the random number table to decide position within the block (e.g. 79 m north and 551 m east from the south-west corner).

In areas where the deer range is composed of large homogeneous blocks of each habitat type and where deer habitat use is likely to vary little between representative blocks of any given habitat type, stratified systematic sampling may be used, e.g. for roe in first rotation upland forests. A large representative block of each habitat should be selected and sample plots located along a transect line passing through the block, starting at a readily located point at the edge of the block. The plots should be spaced equally along the transect a minimum of 50 m apart. Transects should start at the edge of a block or compartment to ensure that the habitat edge is included within the sampling regime. As 'edges' are often heavily used by deer, they should be sampled in proportion to their presence in the area.

Table 3.6   *Sample plot allocation (proportional sampling) for habitat 1*

Block	Area (ha)	Running total (ha)	Number of plots
a	15	15	
b	5	20	
c	25	45	1
d	20	65	2
e	55	120	1
f	10	130	
g	110	240	1
h	25	265	1
i	25	290	
j	60	350	1
k	6	356	
l	4	360	
m	35	395	
n	65	460	2
o	90	550	1

48

Plate 1 *Example of an area suitable for vantage point count, looking across a valley. [B. MAYLE]*

Plate 2 *Handheld thermal imager. [R. GILL]*

Plate 3 *Thermal image of roe deer. [PILKINGTON OPTRONICS LTD]*

Plate 4 *Close up of deer slots in soil. [41876]*

Plate 5 *Deer path through bottom of hedge. [41850]*

Plate 6 *Fused pellet group.* [41732]

Muntjac

Roe

Fallow

Grey squirrel

Rabbit

Sheep

Plate 7 *Pellet groups from rabbit, sheep, squirrels and three deer species.* [41839]

Plate 8 *Red deer pellet group.*
[A. CHADWICK]

Plate 9 *Muntjac pellet group.*
[41554]

Plate 10 *Roe deer pellet group.* *[41735]*

Plate 11 *Fallow deer pellet group.* *[41481]*

Plate 12 *Sika deer pellet group. [51971]*

Plate 13 *Sheep pellet group. [41843]*

Plate 14 *Muntjac latrine. [41551]*

Plate 15 *Roe deer faecal pellet group, almost decayed. [42071]*

13. Index of deer presence

Method

The deer range can be sampled using either a specified number of plots or a specified length of transect within representatives of each habitat. Plots are generally allocated at random within the habitat, while the start point and directions of transects may be allocated at random or systematically, e.g. diagonally SW to NE across a wood (see Sampling in Section 2). Each plot or transect is systematically searched and the number of pellet groups present is recorded by species, where possible. Where more than one species of deer or sheep or goats are present it will probably not be possible to identify all pellet groups to species (Appendix 6). The results (mean or total number of pellet groups per species per transect or plot) can be compared between habitats within and between sites to provide an index of deer presence (high, medium, low).

Data recorded   Number of faecal pellet groups per plot or transect length by species.

Equipment required   Compass, measuring tape and pegs (to set up plots).

H & S considerations   Strong disposable gloves should be worn when searching the undergrowth for faecal pellet groups.

Advantages
- Applicable in any habitat type.
- Not restricted by weather (other than snowfall).
- Quick method (especially if transects used).
- Low labour requirement (1 person).
- Low equipment costs.

Disadvantages
- Only an index can be calculated.
- No age or sex classification possible.

Performance as an estimate	*
Performance as an index	****
Inexpensive equipment costs	*****
Inexpensive labour costs	*****
Simple data analysis	****
Data collection period	1-4 days

Example

A transect method was used to obtain an index of deer presence in woodlands in East Anglia during 1997. For each woodland visited a transect (minimum length 1 km) was walked through the middle following the compass bearing which bisected the wood through its longest axis. All pellet groups found within 0.5 m either side of the line being walked were identified to species, where possible, and recorded. If the transect was less than 1 km then a second transect at right angles to the first was completed. The mean number of pellet groups per 100 m was calculated for each deer species.

14. Clearance counts (FAR)

Clearance counts are most suitable in sites of high deer density (>30 km⁻²) where faecal pellet groups quickly accumulate on the ground.

Method

The deer range should be clearly identified on a map (1:10 000) and stratified into the constituent habitat types. Sample plots should be allocated to each habitat as previously described (page 11). Plots up to 7 m x 7 m in size can be effectively searched by one person and 10 m x 10 m plots are suitable where two people are involved. Larger plots are more likely to contain pellet groups on the second visit.

Plots should be located from the map using a compass bearing from a readily identified point and following this into the area for the specified distance. The distance into the area can be paced while the plot should be marked accurately with a stake or peg placed at each corner to ensure that it will be easily located on the second visit.

The plot should be carefully and systematically searched for faecal pellet groups, which should be removed. Dividing the plot into 1 m strips which are systematically searched is the most practicable searching technique. If two people work together they should start at diagonally opposite corners and both search the whole plot. The number of groups located during this initial search may also be recorded, to allow a population estimate based on standing crop data (see 15 and 16).

Fresh pellet groups found within or close to the plot should be clearly marked to enable any decay between visits to be estimated. Ideally six fresh groups per habitat type should be marked. The procedure should be continued until all sample plots have been checked and cleared.

All plots should be visited a second time and the number of pellet groups accumulated since the first visit counted. The timing of the second visit should be such that the number of pellet groups counted will be maximised and accuracy and efficiency increased. Where previous decay data are available the second visit should be just before the expected decay time (but before there is a need to make large adjustments to the results due to numbers of deer dying naturally or culled between visits). By monitoring the presence of the marked pellet groups for each habitat it will be possible to decide when the most suitable time for the second visit will be. Tables A7.1–A7.7 in Appendix 7 indicate decay lengths measured for faecal pellet groups since 1995 in a range of habitat types. Decay length will tend to be shorter in open habitats and particularly if there has been heavy rainfall, or generally warm, moist conditions. If no decay information is available a period of 2–3 months is usually acceptable.

On the second visit the marked groups should be examined to determine whether there has been any loss of pellet groups due to decay between the two visits. If so, then the figure for accumulated faecal pellet groups should be adjusted to take account of the decay. Deer density for each habitat is calculated from the mean number of pellet groups per hectare, species-specific defecation rate (Appendix 8) and the number of days between the clearance and second count, using the following equation:

Number of deer per ha =

$$\frac{\text{Number of pellet groups per ha}}{\text{Time between visits} \times \text{Defecation rate}}$$
$$\quad\quad\text{(days)}\quad\quad\text{(pellet groups per day)}$$

The use of a computer program speeds up the calculation of population size and confidence intervals from clearance count data. Suitable programmes are available from the authors.

Data recorded　　Number of pellet groups, by species, accumulated for each plot on the second visit and any decay or loss of marked groups.

Equipment required　　Orienteering compass, tape measure, tent pegs or pins, posts, gloves.

H & S considerations　　Strong disposable gloves should be worn when searching vegetation for or handling faecal pellet groups.

Advantages
- Applicable in all habitats and weathers (except snowfall).
- Accuracy and reliability of estimate is higher than for faecal pellet standing crop counts.
- Population estimate for a specific period of time equal to the period between visits.
- Low labour requirement (1-2 people).
- Low equipment costs.
- Easily repeated.

Disadvantages
- Species identification may be difficult where two or more ungulates are present (Appendix 6).

- No indication of sex- or age-class ratios.
- Habitat specific decay should be monitored.
- Delay in obtaining estimate (2-3 months).
- Two site visits required.

Performance as an estimate	*****
Performance as an index	*****
Inexpensive equipment costs	*****
Inexpensive labour costs	**
Simple data analysis	****
Data collection period	2-3 months

Example

Clearance counts were carried out in a deciduous (oak and hazel) woodland with a sparse understorey to estimate the resident roe deer population size. Previous studies at the site indicated a decay period of 1-2 months. Plots totalling 0.37 ha in area were cleared during March and left for 10 days. On the second visit, a total of 40 pellet groups were counted in the 0.37 ha. No decay occurred during the 10 day period between clearance and checking. Assuming 20 pellet groups per day defecation rate for roe deer and 10 days between visits, the population size was estimated as follows:

Number of deer per ha =

$$\frac{\text{Number of pellet groups per ha}}{\text{Time between visits} \times \text{Defecation rate}}$$
$$\quad\quad\text{(days)}\quad\quad\text{(pellet groups per day)}$$

$$= \frac{108.108}{10 \times 20} = 0.54 \text{ per ha}$$

The population density of roe deer in the area was therefore estimated as 54 km^{-2}.

The period between visits in this example (10 days) is much shorter than generally recommended, due to prior knowledge of decay on the site and high deer densities. A period of 3 months or more (depending on habitat specific decay length) is recommended.

15. Standing crop plot counts

This method is best suited to areas of medium deer density (10–30 km^{-2}).

Method

As with 14 (Clearance plots), once the deer range has been stratified, plots should be allocated proportionally to the various habitats, and allocated randomly to representatives of the strata and within each representative.

Plot size and number will depend upon the level of accuracy required and resources available. Plots measuring 7 m x 7 m are recommended as these can be effectively searched by one person without the task becoming too tedious. Larger plots can be searched effectively by two people. If more, smaller plots are used, proportionally more time will be spent finding plot locations. Search time per plot will depend on pellet group density, plot size and how much ground vegetation is present. For example, the search time for one person searching 7 m x 7 m plots in an upland conifer forest was up to 95 minutes per plot with a maximum of 35 pellet groups found in one plot (Smith and Mayle, 1994). However, where ground vegetation is reduced two or three 8 plot transects can be searched by two people in a day (Lavin, personal communication).

At the site, plots should be located from the map by following a compass bearing, from a readily identified point, into the area for the required distance. The plot should be marked out using a tape measure and pegs. It is not necessary to permanently mark plots unless you wish to return to the same plots in following years.

Each plot should be carefully and systematically searched for faecal pellet groups, as previously described (page 50), ensuring that the method of searching is the same as that used to monitor faecal pellet decay. Dividing the plot into 1 metre strips for searching is the most practical searching technique. All faecal pellet groups found should be identified to species (where possible) and recorded (Appendix 9). If two people work together they should start working diagonally opposite each other, with both searching the whole plot. Results should be compared at the end of the plot to ensure that searching standards are the same.

The procedure should be continued until all sample plots have been checked. The mean number of pellet groups per plot is then calculated for each habitat and deer density calculated from the mean number of pellet groups per hectare, habitat-specific decay rates (Appendix 7) and species-specific defecation rates (Appendix 8) using the following equation:

Number of deer per ha =

$$\frac{\text{Number of pellet groups per ha}}{\begin{array}{c}\text{Average decay} \\ \text{time (days) for} \\ \text{a pellet group}\end{array} \times \begin{array}{c}\text{Defecation rate} \\ \text{(pellet groups} \\ \text{per day)}\end{array}}$$

From a knowledge of the area of each habitat type within the deer range and the habitat specific densities it is then possible to calculate an overall population size and density within stated confidence limits (usually calculated to 80% confidence intervals) (see Stratified sampling example). The program 'Pellet 2' available from the authors is recommended for these calculations although these can be done by hand.

Data recorded   For each plot, number of faecal pellet groups per deer species or unknown category. Habitat and species specific faecal pellet decay length.

Equipment required   Orienteering compass, measuring tape and tent pegs/pins (to mark out plot).

H & S considerations   Disposable gloves should be worn when searching vegetation for and handling faecal pellet groups.

Advantages
- Suitable for large areas.
- Suitable for most habitat types.
- Not restricted by weather (other than snowfall).
- Confidence intervals for the population estimate can be calculated.
- More precise than clearance counts.
- Population densities and size estimated for the number of animals continuously using the area over a period of time equal to decay length (usually at least 3-6 months).

- Only one site visit required to count pellet groups.
- In upland habitats it is possible for 2 people to visit and check two or three 8 plot transects in a day (assuming 7 m x 7 m plots).
- Low labour requirement (1-2 people required).
- Low equipment costs.
- Habitat use can be investigated.

Disadvantages
- Habitat and species specific decay rates need to be monitored prior to counts to enable deer density to be calculated.
- Accuracy influenced by accuracy of defecation and decay estimates.
- No sex- or age-class information.
- Species identification may be difficult where two or more ungulates are present (Appendix 6).

Performance as an estimate	****
Performance as an index	*****
Inexpensive equipment costs	*****
Inexpensive labour costs	***
Simple data analysis	***
Data collection period	4-12 months [a]

[a] Previously recorded decay ratescan be used to reduce the collection period to 4–7 days.

Example

Standing crop counts were made for a roe deer population in a North Scotland upland forest. Results are shown in Table 3.7.

Table 3.7 *Estimation of roe deer population size at Glen Righ from faecal pellet standing crop counts*

Habitat strata and count	Mean number of pellets	n	SD	SE	Decay days	Deer (n ha^{-1})	Area (ha)	Total deer	SE
Pre-thicket 3,7,16,13,1,10,10,12	9.0	8	5.07	1.79	183.0	0.50	100.0	50.2	10.00
Restock 8,3,2,3,0,6,5,1	3.5	8	2.67	0.94	91.5	0.39	90.0	35.1	9.48
Thicket 10,5,7,7,9,8,9,5	7.5	8	1.85	0.65	183.0	0.42	220.0	92.0	8.03
Pre-fell 2,3,1,0,1,2,3,2	1.8	8	1.04	0.37	183.0	0.10	340.0	33.2	6.94
Open 1,1,2,0,2,2,1,1	1.2	8	0.71	0.25	91.5	0.14	200.0	27.0	5.58
Total 184 pellet groups							950.0	238.4	18.26

Population density (deer km^{-2}; mean ± SE) = 25.1 ± 1.9.
80% CI = 238 ± t_{35} × 18.26 = 238 ± 24 (215–262 deer).

16. Standing crop strip transect counts

This sampling method is best suited to areas of low deer density (1–10 km^{-2}). It is a long thin plot 500–2000 m x 1 m in size. As the procedure involves recording pellet groups found within each 10m length of 1m wide transect it is effectively a plot sampling method with plots located next to each other.

Method

The deer range should be identified and, if considered necessary, stratified. The length of each transect will depend upon the level of precision required. For a more precise population estimate a longer transect is required, i.e. 2000 m rather than 500 m. For each habitat, a representative compartment should be selected. Transect lines should be marked on the map so that they pass through representative areas of the habitat but do not run parallel to streams, rides, topographic or other features which may influence deer habitat use.

Where the compartment or block is on a valley side and deer may use the lower areas more than the upper areas, transects should run downhill. Transects are best located at random using random number tables (Appendix 1) to determine the start point from a specified (e.g. north-west) corner of the block. The number of transect lines will depend upon their individual lengths and the total transect length to be sampled. In the example shown in Figure 3.11, three lines are required to achieve 2000 m sample length.

At the site the start point should be located and the map bearing transferred to an orienteering compass. Walk 10 m along the bearing and record the number of pellet groups, by species, in the first section (1 m wide x 10 m long) on the survey form (Appendix 10a). A 1 m long cane or rule should be used to measure the transect width, and the compass bearing followed rigidly to ensure minimum bias or selectivity is introduced. Laying a string trail (using a Walktac: see Appendix 5) or pulling a length of wire behind as the compass bearing is followed enables the midpoint of the transect to be determined. Pellet groups found on the edge of a transect or plot should be counted or rejected, based on the number of pellets in the group lying inside or outside the search area. When groups lie exactly on the edge, they should be alternately included and rejected. Individual pellets may belong to 'stringers' which pass across the strip. Care should be taken when searching to ensure these pellets are not missed.

Walk the next 10 m section and record the second section. Repeat until 500 m or 2000 m have been covered, depending on the accuracy required. Add up the total number of pellet groups and read the deer density from Appendix 10b, Table A10.1 or A10.2, depending on the deer species and defecation rate (see Appendix 8 and Table A8.1). The density is more accurately calculated using this equation:

Number of animals per ha =

$$\frac{\text{Number of pellet groups per ha}}{\begin{array}{cc}\text{Defecation rate} & \text{Average decay} \\ \text{(pellet groups} \quad \times & \text{time (days)} \\ \text{per day)} & \text{for a pellet group}\end{array}}$$

This can then be used with knowledge of the area of each habitat to estimate overall deer population size and density.

Although potentially a quicker method than standing crop plot counts, in practice where there is ground vegetation, searching times are similar to plot counts. Where there is no ground vegetation (e.g. under thicket and prefell Sitka spruce), this method is quicker than plot counts. Unless a number of transects are sampled in each habitat, confidence intervals cannot be estimated.

Data recorded   Number of pellet groups, by species, in each 10 m length. Habitat and species-specific faecal pellet decay lengths.

Equipment required   Orienteering compass, Walktac (see Appendix 5, list of equipment suppliers) or wire and a measuring tape, 1 m cane.

H & S considerations   Disposable gloves should be worn when searching for and handling faecal pellet groups.

Advantages

- Suitable for large areas.
- Suitable for most habitats.
- Not restricted by weather (other than snowfall).
- Population estimate is for a period (3–6 months at least).
- Large areas sampled relatively quickly, particularly where ground vegetation is sparse.
- Habitat use may be indicated.
- Low labour requirement (1-2 people).
- Only one site visit to count pellet groups.
- Low equipment costs.
- Most useful in sites of low deer density.

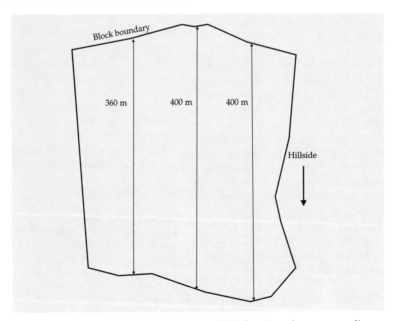

Figure 3.11   *Location of transect lines within a block for strip and transect sampling*

Disadvantages

- Confidence intervals cannot be estimated unless a number of transects are sampled in each habitat.
- Habitat and species-specific decay needs to be monitored before counts and finding sufficient fresh pellet groups may be a problem.
- Precision influenced by accuracy of defecation and decay estimates.
- Unless sampling protocol is followed strictly, there may be a tendency to veer off the transect line towards pellet groups (this will cause bias, and possibly over-estimation of population size).
- No sex- or age-class information.

Performance as an estimate	***
Performance as an index	****
Inexpensive equipment costs	*****
Inexpensive labour costs	***
Simple data analysis	****
Data collection period	4-12 months [a]

[a] Previously recorded decay rates can be used to reduce the collection period to 4–7 days.

Example

Strip transects were used to estimate population density and size for red and roe deer in a 907 ha area in north-west Scotland during March/April 1997. Two men completed seven 800 m x 1 m transects over a $2\frac{1}{2}$ day period (3 transects per man per day). The results are given in Table 3.8.

Table 3.8 *Estimation of deer population size at Lochaber from strip transect faecal pellet counts (800 m)*

Habitat strata	Number of pellet groups		Deer density (km^{-2})		Area (ha)	Total deer	
	Roe deer	Red deer	Roe deer	Red deer		Roe deer	Red deer
Native pinewood	4	12	2.4	5.7	211	5.0	12.0
Establishment	48	6	28.6 }26.8	2.8 }5.0	107	28.7	5.4
Establishment	42	15	25.0	7.1			
Pre-thicket	19	6	11.3	2.9	121	13.7	3.5
Thicket	25	12	14.9 }14.9	5.7 }4.8	200	29.8	9.6
Thicket	25	8	14.9	3.8			
Pre-fell	30	4	17.9	1.9	268	48.0	5.1
Total					907	125	35

Population density of roe deer 13.78 km^{-2}.
Population density of red deer 3.86 km^{-2}.

17. Standing crop line transect counts

Faecal pellet groups may also be counted using the distance sampling techniques described in Section 2. Transect length will depend upon expected pellet group density and required accuracy.

Method

The area to be sampled should be stratified as previously discussed (see Stratified sampling) and a random system of transects superimposed on each area to be sampled (see Figure 3.11).

At the site the start point should be located and the map bearing of the transect transferred to an orienteering compass. The compass bearing should be followed for a predetermined distance, while pellet group presence, for each deer species, and distance from the line is recorded. As with strip transects it will be necessary to locate the line of the compass bearing using a Walktac, string, wire or by having two observers, one a few metres behind the other, so that the line is accurately located before the distance to the observed pellet group is measured. The distance recorded should be the perpendicular distance from the 'centre' of the faecal pellet group (the mid point between the two most widely spaced pellets in the group) to the transect line (Figure 3.11).

Computer models are then used to estimate the probability that a pellet group located within the area will be detected and hence estimate pellet group density in the area (Buckland, 1992; Buckland *et al.*, 1993).

Pellet group density is estimated as follows:

Pellet group density =

$$\frac{\text{Total number of pellet groups detected}}{2 \times \text{Effective 'half-width' of the strip} \times \text{Total length of transect line walked}}$$

Deer density is then estimated based on knowledge of defecation and decay rates, as for plot counts (14).

Data recorded   Number of pellet groups and distance of each group from the line for each deer species. Habitat and species-specific pellet group decay lengths.

Equipment required   Orienteering compass, Walktac or wire and measuring tape.

H & S considerations   Disposable gloves should be worn when searching vegetation for and handling faecal pellet groups.

Advantages
- Suitable for large areas.
- Suitable for all habitats.
- Not limited by weather (except snow cover).
- Precision can be determined.
- Sample sizes are greater than for strip counts.
- Relatively quick compared to plot counts especially at low densities.
- Potentially more accurate than plots in habitats where dense ground vegetation occurs or there is variation in ground vegetation.
- Low labour requirement (2 people).
- Low equipment costs.

Disadvantages
- Accuracy depends upon accurate measurement of perpendicular distance from pellet group to the transect line.
- No sex-/age-class information.
- Slower than strip counts.
- Requires use of specialist computer software to analyse data and calculate population density.

Performance as an estimate	****
Performance as an index	*****
Inexpensive equipment costs	*****
Inexpensive labour costs	***
Simple data analysis	*
Data collection period	4-12 months [a]

[a] Previously recorded decay rates can be used to reduce the collection period to 4–7 days.

Example

The method was used by the Deer Commission for Scotland to estimate sika deer population sizes in a part of south Scotland. The area was divided into eight similarly sized blocks, within which transect lines were placed in a zigzag fashion, 200 m apart. Greater survey effort was allocated to blocks where sika deer density was considered to be highest. Faecal pellet groups were counted and pellet group density for each block estimated. Density was calculated based on an assumed defecation rate of 25 pellet groups per day and decay times which had been monitored for 16 months prior to the faecal pellet count. Densities ranged from 1.38 (95% CI, 0.86–2.2) deer km^{-2} to 20.94 (95% CI, 17.21–25.49) deer km^{-2}.

To achieve this level of accuracy (95% confidence intervals), 26 man-days of effort were required for 10.35 km of transects.

Using cull information

Clear and concise mortality and fertility records for a deer population are invaluable as a means of *retrospectively* calculating population size. They can also be used as a basis for predicting likely future changes in population size. The methods generally rely on knowing the sex and age of all dead animals, and so accuracy will be influenced by the number of animals which die and are not found, any emigration and the accuracy of age determination.

The number of animals culled in any year can only provide an indication of the minimum population size before the cull, e.g. if the cull was 120 animals in total then the minimum population must have been 120 animals before the cull. For deer populations using woodland habitats a cull of 10–25% is usually required to keep the population stable, depending upon natural mortality and fertility levels.

A regular cull (mortality) level, with constant sex- and age-class ratios, achieved over a number of consecutive years may indicate that the population is stable or growing, particularly if there have been no changes in culling effort or habitat quality. However, more detailed information about both the animals culled or dying and the remaining population is required before making any attempt to estimate true population size.

Population reconstruction from mortality data

If all animals dying (culled or natural mortality) are found and aged (for ageing methods, see Chapman and Chapman, 1997; Ratcliffe, 1987; Ratcliffe and Mayle,

1992), it is possible to reconstruct the population size in a number of ways.

18. Balance sheet

This method relies on having previously determined the number of individuals in the population (by sex- and age-class) using a visual method (open hill counts), together with knowledge of sex- and age-class specific deaths. Although the technique provides a quick estimate to predict population size, the estimate will be influenced by the accuracy of the initial population estimate, any bias in sex-class or age-class classification (see 1. Open hill counts), and the proportion of deaths which are not recorded. The method also assumes there is no immigration/emigration, i.e. a 'closed' population.

Method

The deer population range (for both males and females) is first identified and marked on a map. During the spring and autumn of year 1 visual counts to estimate population size and the number of individuals in each sex-/age-class are carried out. All deaths (natural and culled) are recorded by sex- and age-class, and the adult population in year 2 is predicted by subtracting known deaths in any age-/sex-class from the observed population in year 1.

Data recorded   Age- and sex-class of all deer seen during the census, found dead or culled.

Equipment required   Binoculars, telescope, map of area.

H & S considerations   Disposable gloves should be worn when handling and ageing lower jaws of dead animals.

Advantages
- Suitable for all habitats.
- Not limited by weather.
- Sex- and age-class ratios estimated.
- Provides comparison data for other census methods.
- Encourages detailed record collection.

Disadvantages
- Requires visual census and cull data.
- Accuracy influenced by accuracy of original census and mortality data.
- Assumption of 'closed' population probably invalid.

Performance as an estimate	**
Performance as an index	***
Inexpensive equipment costs	***
Inexpensive labour costs	**
Simple data analysis	***
Data collection period	6-9 months

Example

A woodland population of roe deer was observed on one day during October prior to the doe cull. A total of 187 individual deer were seen (62 males, 125 females). Seventy-four does (kids and adults) were culled over winter and the population censused visually, using the same observers and technique in the following March. Two hundred and eighty-eight deer were observed at this time (104 males, 184 females). Given the initial observations and the known cull of 74 females, the expected number of deer to be seen in the following spring would be 113 (62 males and 51 females). However, the observed animals were 104 males and 184 females, suggesting that either the initial survey was inaccurate and a large number had been missed, or that 175 new animals had moved into the area during the winter.

Assuming no immigration over winter, from the spring observation data (104 males and 184 females) and the known cull of 74 females, the minimum precull population must have been 362 or almost twice the number observed in October. This emphasises the problems associated with single sample visual censuses, and the main reason why they are not recommended.

19. Life tables

If the age and sex of *all* deer dying (natural or culled) over a number of years is recorded it is then possible to reconstruct the population for any year in the past. The exact number of deer in any age class in any given year can then be calculated. The probability of an animal surviving from birth to any given age can then be estimated and used to calculate other parameters. If it can be assumed that these age-specific survival rates are still valid then they can be used to estimate current population size (Lowe, 1969; Caughley, 1977; Boyce, 1995). In reality it is rarely possible to find *all* dead animals, but it can be assumed that *most* are found (e.g. in parks) then accuracy will be high.

Life tables are termed 'time-specific' or 'static' when calculated from data on age composition of a population at a specific point in time representing all age-groups in the population. If calculated by following an age-group or 'cohort' through time, they are known as 'cohort' or 'dynamic' life tables (see 20). Static life tables are only valid where the age-class distribution of the population remains stable over the period equal to the oldest cohort in the population. Where juvenile survival rates fluctuate from year to year (e.g. roe deer: Ratcliffe and Mayle, 1992) age-class distribution will vary between years and static life tables are not valid.

Data recorded   Sex- and age-class of all deer seen during the census, found dead or culled.

Equipment required   For roe and fallow, age determination (see Chapman and Chapman, 1997; Ratcliffe, 1987; Ratcliffe and Mayle, 1992).

H & S considerations   Disposable gloves should be worn when handling and ageing lower jaws of dead animals.

Advantages
- Suitable for all habitats.
- Sex- and age-class ratios can be estimated.
- Low labour requirement.
- Low equipment costs.
- Encourages detailed record keeping.

Disadvantages
- Accuracy influenced by bias and accuracy in age determination methods and the proportion of animals dying and not recorded.
- Assumption of 'closed' population (no emigration or immigration) may not be valid.
- Retrospective rather than current population estimated.
- Requires data collection over a period of years.
- Requires experience in fitting mathematical models.

Performance as an estimate	***
Performance as an index	****
Inexpensive equipment costs	****
Inexpensive labour costs	**
Simple data analysis	**
Data collection period	5+ years

20. Cohort analysis

For a given deer population, from knowledge of age at death it is possible to determine year of birth and then accumulate over a period of years the total number of individuals born in any specified (cohort) year (Ratcliffe, 1987; Ratcliffe and Mayle, 1992). Appendix 11 (record form) shows the format for data recording. The number of animals dying in each age class are entered in the vertical column for each year. Lines are totalled horizontally to give the number of animals dying from any particular cohort. The total animals recovered from a given cohort year can then be used, with fertility and mortality data, to calculate the number of young which must have been born in that year, and hence the number of reproducing females in the population. Information on adult sex ratios allows a minimum population size to be calculated for the cohort year. At least 5 consecutive years' worth of mortality data should be collected before population reconstruction is attempted as only by then can it be assumed that a reasonably large proportion of animals born in year 1 will have been recovered. The method can be applied wherever there is good fertility, mortality and sex ratio data for the population, and is particularly useful where most deaths are from culling.

Data recorded   Sex and age of all deer found dead or culled.

H & S considerations   Disposable gloves should be worn when handling and ageing lower jaws of dead animals.

Advantages
- Suitable for all habitats.
- Sex- and age-class ratios can be estimated.

- Low labour requirement.
- Low equipment costs.
- Encourages detailed record keeping.
- Useful for retrospectively checking the accuracy of other methods.

Disadvantages
- Accuracy influenced by biases in age determination and the proportion of animals dying and not recorded.
- At least 5 years before a population estimate can be calculated.
- Retrospective (but can be used predictively with 18, 19 and 21).

Performance as an estimate	****
Performance as an index	****
Inexpensive equipment costs	*****
Inexpensive labour costs	**
Simple data analysis	**
Data collection period	5+ years

Example

Figure 3.12 shows the cohort analysis for roe does from Alice Holt Forest, south-east England (Ratcliffe and Mayle, 1992). By 1988, 26 female deer had been recovered from the 1978 cohort. As a 1:1 sex ratio is common at birth, 26 male kids would probably also have been born in 1978. Survival data suggest 0.75 survival to the winter, therefore $52 \div 0.75$ = the total number of kids born in 1978, i.e. 69. The number of reproducing females required to produce these kids depends on fertility levels. If this is 1.5 kids per doe, then $69 \div 1.5 = 46$ breeding age females must have been present. Roe populations generally have a 1:1 sex ratio, therefore there would probably have been 46 males of the same age.

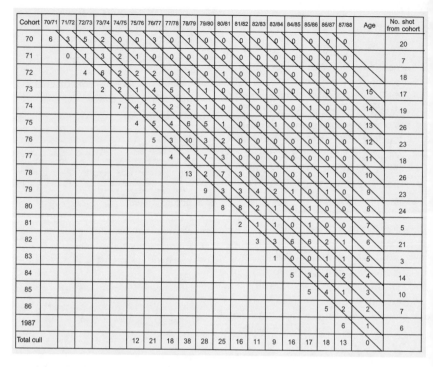

Figure 3.12   *Cohort analysis for roe does, Alice Holt Forest*

The number of non-breeding (yearling) does present = the number of animals recovered from the 1977 cohort minus the number shot as kids (i.e. 18 - 4 = 14). If we assume there were the same number of yearling bucks present, the total population just after the birth pulse in 1978 can be estimated as 46 adult males, 46 adult females, 28 yearlings (males + females) and 69 kids.

The total minimum population estimate for 1978 is therefore 189.

21. Population modelling

Computer models (Leslie, 1945 and 1948) based on estimates of current population size, fertility and age-specific mortality can be used to predict post-breeding population size in future years. *The accuracy of predictions relies on accurate estimates of initial population size, sex and age-class ratios, age-class specific fertility and mortality levels.* One such model is available from the authors. Models which include habitat quality influences on fertility and mortality levels are now becoming available (Buckland *et al.*, 1998). Population modelling is used as a routine and integral part of deer population management by Forest Enterprise in North Scotland.

Advantages
- Suitable for all habitats and species.
- Sex- and age-class ratios can be estimated.
- Encourages detailed record-keeping.
- Different culling scenarios can be quickly evaluated and tested against true population information.
- Low labour requirement.
- Predictive
- Implications of changes in mortality, fertility and age structure are easily shown.

Disadvantages
- Accuracy influenced by accuracy of initial population estimate, age-class ratios and age-specific fertility and mortality data (which may vary annually).
- Requires use of computer and suitable software.

Performance as an estimate	*****
Performance as an index	*****
Inexpensive equipment costs	***
Inexpensive labour costs	**
Simple data analysis	**
Data collection period	1+ years

Example

A roe deer population of 238 animals was modelled based on the following assumptions:

1:1 sex ratio. Fertility: yearlings 0.9 kids per doe, adult (2–6 years) 1.14 kids per doe, adult (7–9 years) 0.4 kids per doe. Survivorship: kids 0.88, yearlings 0.9, adults (2–6 years) 0.95, adults (7 and 8 years) 0.3.

Table 3.9 shows the predicted population change for females only for 5 years based on this information. The population increases at approximately 25% per year.

Table 3.9 *Predicted population changes (females only) using a Leslie matrix model*

Year	Total population	Age-class								
		K	1	2	3	4	5	6	7	8	9
0	119	34	24	18	14	9	7	6	5	1	1
1	149	43	30	22	17	13	9	7	6	2	0
2	187	54	38	27	21	16	12	9	7	2	1
3	234	68	48	34	26	20	15	11	9	2	1
4	291	84	60	43	32	25	19	14	10	3	1
5	364	106	74	54	41	30	24	18	13	3	1

4 Using Census Data

Accurate census information enables objective decisions to be made about deer population management. These decisions will be based on sound information about which species are present and their estimated densities and numbers.

Where an index of deer numbers indicates that the population is at a medium to high level then it would be advisable to protect newly planted or coppiced areas against deer browsing. As discussed in Section 1, it will be essential to know which deer species are present to ensure effective protection is used. Advice on the height of individual tree protection or fence specifications to protect against specific deer species is available in Hodge and Pepper (1998), Pepper *et al.* (1985) and Pepper (1992).

Accurate population estimates within clearly stated confidence intervals are required where management objectives are to reduce numbers (in order to decrease impact levels and road traffic accidents or improve herd quality) or to crop deer populations. Target culls can then be set based on the overall population size and predicted recruitment rate, estimated from counts of adult females and young (e.g. 1) or from cull data (see 20 and Ratcliffe and Mayle, 1992). Cull setting should also take into consideration the upper and lower limits of the 95% confidence interval, particularly where the confidence limits are wide. A cull based on the overall estimate will be too low if the population is, in fact, at the upper limit, and too high if the population is at the lower limit of the confidence interval. Setting the cull too high will often become evident as it becomes increasingly difficult to achieve. However, if too low a cull is set then the population and its impacts will remain unacceptable or increase, and a larger cull will be required in the next year to reduce the population to the target level. If confidence intervals are large then a second census method on the same site may help to increase the precision of the estimate. Once target culls have been set decisions can then be made about how these are to be achieved, and by whom, particularly where the population is being managed by a Deer Management Group.

Knowledge of population size also enables priorities to be set where a manager is dealing with a number of deer populations, particularly if resources are limited. It may be possible to 'let' stalking for less vulnerable areas while concentrating the limited resources on priority areas.

Deer numbers should be assessed regularly (every 1–2 years) preferably by the same people using the same methods. Monitoring in this way allows the effectiveness of a given culling strategy to be measured against management objectives. Regular population estimates should be an integral part of any long-term strategy to manage a deer population and their habitat. Where only an index of numbers is determined then any population trends will become apparent after a minimum of 8 years. This may help clarify management objectives for the site and deer population. However, knowing just the trend is not sufficient information on which to base a cull.

Collection of census data on deer numbers and sex ratios together with data on, or estimations of, recruitment rate enables a whole series of management scenarios to be simulated by computer (see 21). Different culling regimes to produce the same result can be considered. The effect of the stalker falling ill and only achieving half of his target cull, or retiring and not being replaced, can be investigated. It is possible to model the outcome of not achieving the target cull, and specifically not achieving the target number of males or females. Additionally population changes over time can be predicted with or without changes in habitat structure to allow forward planning of resource requirement and allocation.

As was stated at the beginning of this book, deer populations have been and are likely to continue to increase in size and distribution in the foreseeable future. Managers need to know which species are present and how many there are. Only then can they effectively manage both the deer and their impacts. The authors hope that this book provides the initial step towards sound and effective long-term deer management strategies for the future.

5 Supporting Information

Appendix 1.   Random number table

```
079 551 301   310 461 159   818 853 608   672 203 590   754 571 895   971 265 887
487 075 504   870 468 884   660 070 970   729 505 616   943 880 980   449 970 409
490 778 260   570 039 047   972 907 421   029 676 568   387 019 426   817 271 470
315 968 428   832 661 594   416 539 672   408 300 742   695 026 349   690 930 535
254 686 475   647 147 101   322 432 425   735 897 061   661 978 018   646 115 106

674 156 836   810 092 594   189 346 340   857 794 334   717 195 470   261 229 514
819 969 877   363 635 512   765 016 377   008 940 535   023 904 040   318 094 488
803 813 142   229 099 369   477 025 346   217 930 416   903 937 570   930 893 054
942 388 420   880 037 040   065 883 681   130 316 224   853 197 886   907 031 387
184 016 138   497 263 958   010 994 205   843 968 938   684 754 341   563 200 631

922 488 098   387 143 398   273 748 002   499 491 213   351 281 067   612 330 630
994 864 659   974 305 796   692 855 174   998 282 548   794 344 764   264 210 215
797 844 747   041 433 658   062 922 410   107 154 252   679 874 785   468 084 348
991 861 683   506 573 712   508 300 662   367 341 618   781 025 301   828 014 333
956 895 763   081 950 731   882 981 665   096 260 745   347 212 418   152 877 611

687 338 000   717 523 884   423 725 569   815 977 095   229 727 889   052 264 915
340 101 648   387 543 674   248 467 202   589 050 491   731 523 800   020 846 249
562 962 795   832 028 606   047 005 468   092 583 507   102 249 063   636 305 076
792 015 035   793 243 078   629 521 525   764 691 353   807 819 731   771 749 295
707 849 431   375 911 060   853 385 982   331 979 776   432 333 267   921 693 066

637 131 431   839 538 010   585 553 989   508 228 001   802 899 481   359 400 094
707 823 501   481 137 874   879 124 132   433 318 401   809 846 076   139 274 890
991 060 513   016 462 822   340 366 637   799 777 069   970 624 932   612 439 803
015 368 866   592 747 885   752 528 679   683 603 719   024 258 810   900 359 765
675 769 369   939 184 869   707 327 412   174 932 215   172 678 448   854 145 141

014 268 317   352 641 718   804 564 970   709 771 127   515 609 327   728 508 422
958 358 005   900 675 184   274 833 465   888 643 220   400 249 033   834 257 014
777 600 444   723 017 754   082 491 001   836 058 004   845 742 991   154 035 672
854 144 044   321 442 431   556 823 945   255 051 330   357 243 471   389 002 682
338 861 601   345 147 322   815 243 694   671 345 883   437 938 928   581 100 228

690 811 307   910 255 184   979 534 919   601 985 059   861 922 836   326 065 142
627 550 060   058 401 663   424 122 491   117 986 347   420 066 566   946 788 731
551 477 437   142 134 126   574 169 685   565 451 448   084 837 845   669 254 615
133 515 561   071 023 496   045 432 844   397 006 348   908 382 643   069 711 307
538 271 986   475 739 518   005 216 100   798 522 746   920 635 404   574 184 690

892 938 887   902 151 345   599 033 991   722 213 949   631 060 620   351 058 068
920 510 765   708 105 258   789 960 910   589 210 166   976 259 243   898 525 866
516 098 213   244 481 718   673 361 353   847 867 480   690 938 699   333 714 587
640 324 072   607 732 490   162 193 809   888 980 459   710 321 946   073 553 508
291 089 858   333 561 201   978 748 813   487 071 395   034 656 658   630 590 694
```

Appendix 2. Example habitat stratification

In Alice Holt Forest, Hampshire/Surrey, a very diverse forest, 12 habitat types were recognised on the basis of age-class of trees and vegetation types, which would probably be differentially used by the deer. These were as follows:

Conifer establishment
Conifers 0–5 years old. Mainly Norway spruce (*Picea abies*) and Corsican pine (*Pinus nigra*) less than 1 m high. Ground flora of hazel (*Corylus avellana*), bracken (*Pteridium aquilinum*), bramble (*Rubus fruticosus*) and wavy hair grass (*Deschampsia flexuosa*).

Conifer pre-thicket
Conifers aged 10–20 years old. Mainly Corsican pine, Norway spruce, hybrid larch (*Larix eurolepis*) and western hemlock (*Tsuga heterophylla*). Ground flora of bracken, wavy hair grass and raspberry (*Rubus idaeus*).

Conifer pole-stage
Conifers aged 20–30 years old. Mainly Norway spruce, western hemlock, Corsican pine, hybrid larch and Douglas fir (*Pseudotsuga menziesii*). Ground flora of bracken, bramble, wavy hair grass and dead needles.

Conifer pre-felling
Conifers more than 30 years old. Mainly Corsican pine, western hemlock, Norway spruce, Japanese larch (*Larix kaempferi*). Canopy closed in most places with a reduced ground flora; scattered patches of short bracken and wavy hair grass.

Broadleaved establishment
Broadleaved trees aged 0–3 years. Mainly oak about 1 m high. Ground flora of bramble, hazel, bracken, holly (*Ilex aquifolium*) and Yorkshire fog (*Holcus lanatus*).

Broadleaved pre-thicket
Broadleaved trees aged 4–15 years. Mainly oak about 2.5 m high, interspersed with regenerating hazel. Ground flora of Yorkshire fog, bramble, bilberry (*Vaccinium myrtillus*), willowherb (*Chamaenerion angustifolium*), dog's mercury (*Mercurialis perennis*) and bracken.

Broadleaved thicket
Broadleaved trees aged 15–25 years. A mixture of oak (*Quercus* spp.) with some Norway spruce and hazel. Profuse shrub vegetation with dog's mercury, bramble, wild strawberry (*Fragaria vesca*), ground ivy (*Glechoma hederacea*) and willowherb.

Broadleaved pole-stage
Broadleaved trees aged 25–40 years. A mixture of oak, alder (*Alnus glutinosa*) and beech (*Fagus sylvatica*). Canopy and understorey species of holly, hawthorn (*Crataegus* spp.), yew (*Taxus baccata*) and hazel. Ground flora of bramble, dog's mercury and creeping soft grass (*Holcus mollis*).

Broadleaved pre-felling
Broadleaved trees older than 40 years. A mixture of oak, ash (*Fraxinus excelsior*), sweet chestnut (*Castanea sativa*) and western red cedar (*Thuja plicata*). Canopy and understorey species of hawthorn, yew and hazel. Ground flora of bramble, honeysuckle (*Lonicera periclymenum*), stinging nettle (*Urtica dioica*), wavy hair grass and bracken.

Recently felled broadleaved woodland

Originally oak woodland with hawthorn, hazel and field maple (*Acer campestre*). Newly growing coppiced stumps and ground flora including bramble, raspberry and bracken.

Pasture

A semi-permanent grassland used for hay and grazing. Ground vegetation of dock (*Rumex* spp.), creeping thistle (*Cirsium arvense*), meadow buttercup (*Ranunculus acris*), yarrow (*Achillea millefolium*) and grasses (Gramineae).

Appendix 3. Vantage point count form
Density estimation for woodland deer occupying hilly terrain

Forest_____ Observer(s)_____

Location_____ Area____ha Structural type_____ Planting year_____

Date_____ Time on_____ Time off_____

Weather conditions and visibility_____

DEER SEEN									
Time	Location	Species	Adult male	Adult female	Yearlings male	Yearlings female	Calf/kid	Unclassified	Remarks

Appendix 4. Thermal imaging record form

Forest _____ Start time _____ Finish time _____ Date _____

Observer _____ Weather _____

Block	Route	Route length (m)	Species	Numbers in group					Body	Bearing (deg°)	Direction (deg°)	Perp. dist. (m)	Comments
				Σ	♂	♀	J	♀+J					

See page 73 for explanatory notes.

Thermal imaging record form: explanatory notes

Forest: Name of forest or woodland.

Weather: Mention weather, especially if it is stormy, rainy or windy, or changes during the course of a night.

Block: Letter (e.g. A or B) referring to *a part* of the forest named above (only needed if estimate required for part of the forest).

Route: Route label, e.g. 1, 2, etc.

Length: Length of route or line in metres (measured from 1:10 000 map, e.g. 1500). If observations were made from only one side of the vehicle, then this distance should be divided by 2. Routes from which no deer were seen should also be included.

Species: For example, R=red deer, S=sika deer.

Number: Number of deer in group followed by numbers of sex-/age-classes, if identifiable. Σ=total, ♂=males, ♀=females, J=juveniles, ♀+J=groups of does/hinds plus calves. If the figure put under Σ > ♂+♀+J (or ♂+(♀+J)) then the remainder is assumed unclassifiable.

Body: Length of body, nose–rump, standing side on, measured in graticules, e.g. 1.5. Assumed to be measured on animal at centre of the group. If the group was of mixed sex or included adults+juveniles, enter the sex/age measured under 'comments'. If only the head is visible measure ear–ear width or tine–tine width and mention this in 'comments'. This measurement should be taken from where the group was first sighted. If the animals were approached (e.g. to help identify them) before the body length was measured then the distance moved should be estimated and noted in 'comments'.

Bearing: Bearing° of animal from observer.

Direction: Bearing° of the direction of the route from where the observation was made.

Perp. dist. Distance at right angles (perpendicular) to route/line.

Comments: Any other information. For example: behaviour, or compartment label; enter 'Ride' if on ride or forest road or 'Field' if in neighbour's field; enter direction (N, S, E, W) group took flight, if this may take them near another route/line.

NB

- For *all* groups, enter 'Body' and 'Bearing' and mark the position of the group on 1:10 000 map as accurately as possible, labelling group with the serial number.
- Enter 'Direction' if the route ahead is straight.
- If body length < 0.5 graticules *or* the route bends and the bearing of direction of travel would give a misleading estimate of the perpendicular distance, then mark observer position on the map as well, and measure/confirm perpendicular distance from the map afterwards.

Appendix 5. List of equipment suppliers

Thermal imaging equipment

Pilkington Optronics Ltd
1 Linthouse Road, Glasgow
C51 4BZ

Agema Infrared Systems Ltd
Arden House, West Street
Leighton Buzzard
LU7 7DD

GEC Marconi
Christopher Martin Road
Basildon, Essex
SS14 3EL

Insight Vision Systems
Merebrook
Hanley Road,Malvern
Worcestershire
WR13 6NP

Suitable equipment is also available
for hire from the authors.

Transect equipment

Walktac
Stanton Hope
11 Seax Court, Southfields
Laindon, Basildon, Essex
SS15 6LY

Appendix 6. Faecal pellet group identification

Deer faecal pellets are short, cylindrical or almost spherical, and often have a small point at one end (Figure A6.1). They have a smooth surface compared to faeces of carnivores or rabbits and hares and when fresh are usually black and covered in a thin, shiny layer of mucus which quickly dries. In spring/summer when lush new vegetation is available they may be sticky and softer and individual pellets will often become fused together (Plate 6). The number of pellets defecated in a group at one time will vary due to sex, age-class and diet of the individual animal and may be as many as 150 for fallow deer (Smith and Mayle, 1994). However, the average number of pellets in a fresh group is 40–60.

Figure A6.1 *Typical deer pellet shapes*

Where only one species of deer or ungulate is present faecal pellet identification is not a problem. Deer and rabbit or hare faecal pellets are sufficiently different for there to be no confusion about identification between these species groups (Plate 7).

There is also minimum confusion when trying to distinguish between faecal pellet groups of the largest (red; Plate 8) and smallest (muntjac; Plate 9) deer species. Greatest confusion occurs between muntjac and roe (Plate 10), roe and fallow (Plate 11), fallow and sika (Plate 12), and sika and red deer especially if red/sika hybrids are present. Confusion, particularly with red and roe deer pellets, can also occur if goats or sheep (Plate 13) are also resident in the area.

'Typical' pellet groups for all species are shown in Plates 6–13 and described in the identification section below. However individual pellet and pellet group form will vary due to diet (site and seasonally influenced), age- and sex-class of the animal. For example, pellets produced by mature red deer stags tend to be larger than those produced by hinds and individual pellet shape may also vary. Within any species pellets produced by juveniles will be smaller than those produced by adults.

The most effective means of becoming confident at the identification of pellets is to collect fresh pellets from known species. This can be from deer farms, areas where only one species is known to occur, after watching an animal defecate, or from the rectum of shot deer. Then study their form and ideally get a colleague to place these out in the field to enable a 'blind' test for identification.

In any event, unless there is only one species of ungulate present it is not usually possible to allocate 100% of all pellet groups found with confidence. Most, usually 80–90% of pellet groups, will be allocated to a specific species and the remainder will be allocated to an unknown or possible category, e.g. red/sika, which can then be dealt with separately or assigned to the specific species in the same proportions as the identified faecal pellet groups (Buckland, 1992).

Deer faecal pellet identification

Red deer
Pellets are up to 30 mm long and 13–18 mm across (Staines, 1991; Bang and Dahlstrom, 1974), cylindrical in shape, often with a point at one end and rounded or slightly concave at the other, being described as 'acorn-shaped' by Staines (1991). Usually black and shiny when fresh, they become duller and dark brown as they age.

Sika deer
Pellets are similar to those of red and roe (Ratcliffe, 1991) and fallow (Lowe, 1977).

Fallow deer
Pellets are cylindrical, usually pointed at one end and concave at the other: 16 x 11 mm in males and 15 x 8 mm in females (Chapman and Putman, 1991).

Roe deer
Pellets are elongated and cylindrical in shape, approx. 14 x 6 mm, up to 18 x 9 mm and often stick together when deer have been feeding on readily digested food during the summer (Staines and Ratcliffe, 1991).

Muntjac deer
Pellets are black, shiny and striated, spherical or cylindrical in shape and from 6–13 mm long x 5–11 mm broad. Pellets may be pointed at one or both ends, rounded concave or flat at the other end or rounded at both ends. Fresh groups contain 20–120 pellets which may adhere to each other. In some areas the same spot may be returned to for defecation, forming a latrine site (Plate 14) (Chapman, 1991).

Chinese water deer
Pellets similar to those of muntjac, but usually longer - 10–15 mm x 5–10 mm. Black or dark brown and cylindrical, with a point at one end (Farrell and Cooke, 1991).

Sheep
Similar to, but less regular than goat, pellets measure 12–17 mm x approx. 10 mm. Although initially cylindrical, compression during deposition may cause them to become more angled and sometimes pyramidal in shape (Bang and Dahlstrom, 1974). Large deposits may build up in some sites (Jewell and Bullock, 1991).

Goats
Pellets are similar in shape and size to those of sheep, red and roe deer, 10–20 mm long, cylindrical with pointed or concave ends. Tend to be more symmetrical than deer or sheep pellets and large accumulations build up in traditional shelter spots (Bullock, 1991).

Rabbits and hares
Rabbit and hare pellets are very similar, slightly flattened, spherical and firm, being larger in hares (15–20 mm diameter) than in rabbits (~10 mm diameter). No obvious

mucus covering, so not adherent and coarse fragments of plants can be clearly seen on the surface. Colour varies according to diet, but tends to be paler than deer pellets, and becomes paler as exposed to the sun. Rabbits use faecal pellets as territory markers hence large numbers may be found in one spot (Bang and Dahlstrom, 1974).

Appendix 7. Faecal pellet group decay assessment

The presence of faecal pellet groups in the habitat will be influenced by both the number of deer, their defecation rate and the length of time that pellets remain on the ground (decay time). Pellet groups are subject to a number of influences and may disappear due to microbial or invertebrate attack, the mechanical forces of rain, wind or physical disturbance (by passing animals) or by being covered by vegetation or falling leaf/needle litter. Deer diet and hence pellet form and shelter from climatic influences provided by vegetation on the site, together with soil moisture levels, will also influence decay. Pellet group decay will therefore be species, site and habitat specific and should necessarily be measured for each habitat in sites where faecal pellet groups are to be counted to provide an estimate of deer population size.

Mitchell and McCowan (1984) showed that red deer pellet group decay could vary from 95 to 450 days between sites and seasons, and Smith and Mayle (1994) recorded decays as short as 12 days for fallow deer faecal pellet groups in a site in north-west Wales.

Studies to investigate and model the influence of habitat, season and weather on faecal pellet group decay are under way in Forest Enterprise sites. Six fresh pellet groups have been monitored in each habitat for each month, as described below. Initial results are given in Tables A7.1–A7.5 and are for decay length estimated from faecal pellet groups monitored between March 1995 and August 1997 in a range of habitat types in three climatic zones (wet,

moist, dry, see Figure A7.1) for the five major deer species in Great Britain.

These figures are presented as a *guide* to indicate the variability in decay lengths, and to provide the reader with an 'estimate' of decay which can be used in conjunction with their own faecal pellet group count data, where they do not yet have their own site specific decay data. The figures can be adjusted accordingly, based on 'local' and regional information on climatic variation between years. For example, if summer 1997 was wetter than 1995 then length of time to decay could be expected to be less for an open habitat.

Monitoring faecal pellet group decay

Where decay lengths of ≤6 months are expected faecal pellet group decay need only be monitored for the 6 months prior to standing crop counts (i.e. from September/October onwards if standing crop counts are to be carried out in March/April). Where decay lengths are generally >6 months (see Tables A7.1–A7.5) we advise that decay length is monitored for 12 months or more.

Faecal pellet groups to monitor decay should be collected and placed out on a day when 'typical' weather conditions for that month prevail. Extreme weather conditions should be avoided. They should be placed in a position where 'typical conditions' within the habitat prevail (e.g. if 75% of a pre-thicket area is closed canopy, 75% of the groups should be placed under closed canopy).

Fresh faecal pellet groups should be collected from the habitat in question or neighbouring habitats. A minimum of 4–6 groups, each containing at least 40 pellets, should be placed and marked in the habitat, away from the edge but in a site which can be readily monitored. The date of placement should be recorded and the pellet groups visited regularly (weekly during periods of high rainfall, monthly during 'normal' weather). Fresh pellet groups should be placed out each calendar month.

The presence of each pellet group should be ascertained and recorded on a decay assessment form (Table A7.6). A group is still present if six or more pellets remain (Plate 15). *The searching technique used should be consistent across habitat types and the same as that used for the faecal pellet groups standing crop or clearance crop counts* (i.e. if vegetation is parted or the last leaf fall moved to count the number of pellets in a group when monitoring decay, the same search method should be used for the clearance or standing crop counts).

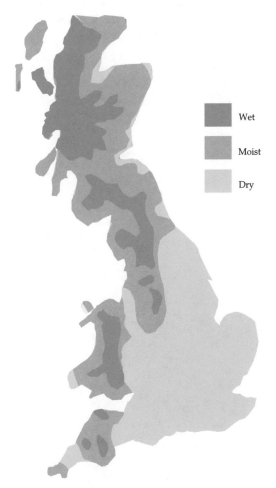

Figure A7.1 *Three moisture zones in Great Britain, based on ecological site classification*

Any tendency to search more diligently for pellet groups which are being monitored for decay rate (as the observer will remember where these were initially placed) should be avoided.

For each pellet group, the number of days to decay should be recorded and the average number of days to decay calculated for the six groups in each habitat for each month. The overall average number of days to decay is calculated by totalling the 12 monthly averages and dividing by 12. Table A7.7 gives an example of 12 months records for one habitat type. Where decay length is so short that only pellet groups from 4 months prior to a March standing crop count would be expected to be present, then only the previous 4 months data should be used to calculate decay length.

The following indicates the importance of accurate decay information:

Assuming the same number of faecal pellet groups per hectare had been found in three habitats (A, B and C) with decays of 12, 95 and 450 days, then the deer densities of B and C would be 1/8 and 1/37.5 that of A.

Table A7.1 *Decay lengths for red deer*

Habitat	Climatic zones (see Figure A7.1)					
	Dry		Moist		Wet	
	Location	Days to decay	Location	Days to decay	Location	Days to decay
Open						
Bare ground						
Grass ride/glade					Sunart	81
Moor/heath					Lochaber	444
					Sunart	146
Grass/pasture						
Woodland						
Establishment/restock					Sunart	149
(up to 1 m top height)						
Conifer						
Pre-thicket	Thetford	96				
(up to 3 m top height)						
Thicket	Thetford	106				
(up to 10 m top height)						
Pole-stage	Thetford	103				
Pre-fell	Thetford	99			Lochaber	177
					Doilet [a]	510
Broadleaf						
Pre-thicket						
(up to 3 m top height)						
Thicket						
(up to 10 m top height)						
Pre-fell						
Mature	Thetford	77				

[a] Pellet groups still present after 1 year.

Table A7.2 *Decay lengths for roe deer*

| Habitat | Climatic zones (see Figure A7.1) | | | | | |
| | Dry | | Moist | | Wet | |
	Location	Days to decay	Location	Days to decay	Location	Days to decay
Open						
Bare ground						
Grass ride/glade			Ayrshire [a]	638		
Riparian						
Moor/heath						
Grass/pasture	Hampshire	64			Hamsterley	98
Woodland						
Establishment/restock (up to 1 m top height)	Hampshire	138	Ayrshire	189	Hamsterley [a]	352
Conifer						
Pre-thicket (up to 3 m top height)	Thetford	78	Ayrshire	202	Hamsterley	371
Thicket (up to 10 m top height)	Thetford	91				
Pole-stage	Thetford	77			Hamsterley	370
Pre-fell	Thetford	92	Ayrshire [a]	416	Hamsterley	537
Broadleaf						
Pre-thicket (up to 3 m top height)						
Thicket (up to 10 m top height)	Hampshire	165				
Pre-fell					Hamsterley	196
Mature	Thetford	75				
	Hampshire 1 [b]	111				
	Hampshire 2 [c]	129				

[a] Pellet groups still present after 1 year.
[b] Ground vegetation grassy.
[c] Ground vegetation leaf litter.

Table A7.3 *Decay lengths for sika deer*

Habitat	Dry		Moist		Wet	
	Location	Days to decay	Location	Days to decay	Location	Days to decay
Open						
Bare ground			Peebleshire	135		
Grass ride/glade						
Riparian						
Moor/heath						
Grass/pasture						
Woodland						
Establishment/restock						
(up to 1 m top height)						
Conifer						
Pre-thicket			Peebleshire[a]	134		
(up to 3 m top height)						
Thicket						
(up to 10 m top height)						
Pole-stage			Peebleshire	219		
Pre-fell						
Broadleaf						
Pre-thicket						
(up to 3 m top height)						
Thicket						
(up to 10 m top height)						
Pre-fell						
Mature						

[a] Pellet groups still present after 1 year.

Table A7.4 *Decay lengths for fallow deer*

Habitat	Climatic zones (see Figure A7.1)					
	Dry		Moist		Wet	
	Location	Days to decay	Location	Days to decay	Location	Days to decay
Open						
Bare ground			Ae	240		
Grass ride/glade	New Forest	99	West Glamorgan	57		
Riparian			West Glamorgan	89		
Moor/heath					Dolgellau	340
Arable crops						
Grass/pasture			Ae	42		
Woodland						
Establishment/restock (up to 1 m top height)					Dolgellau	124
Conifer						
Pre-thicket (up to 3 m top height)			West Glamorgan	114	Dolgellau	198
Thicket (up to 10 m top height)					Dolgellau	270
Pole-stage	New Forest	265			Dolgellau[a]	434
Pre-fell					Dolgellau	171
Broadleaf						
Pre-thicket (up to 3 m top height)						
Thicket (up to 10 m top height)						
Pre-fell						
Mature	New Forest	219				

[a] Pellet groups still present after 1 year.

Table A7.5 *Decay lengths for muntjac deer*

Habitat	Climatic zones (see Figure A7.1)					
	Dry		Moist		Wet	
	Location	Days to decay	Location	Days to decay	Location	Days to decay
Open						
Bare ground						
Grass ride/glade						
Riparian						
Moor/heath						
Grass/pasture						
Woodland						
Establishment/restock (up to 1 m top height)						
Conifer						
Pre-thicket (up to 3 m top height)	Thetford	89		No data available		
Thicket (up to 10 m top height)	Thetford	99				
Pole-stage	Thetford	102				
Pre-fell	Thetford	128				
Broadleaf						
Pre-thicket (up to 3 m top height)						
Thicket (up to 10 m top height)						
Pre-fell						
Mature	Thetford	100				

Table A7.6 *Faecal pellet group decay assessment form*

Deer species _____   Forest _____   Ground vegetation _____

Location _____   Habitat type _____

Date located _____

Inspection date   DD/MM/YY

Table A7.7 *Pellet decay : example of 12 months' records*

	Aug	Sep	Oct	Nov	Dec	Jan	Feb	Mar	Apr	May	Jun	Jul
Sep	123456											
Oct		123456										
Nov			123456									
Dec			x x	123456								
Jan		x	x		123456							
Feb						123456						
Mar			x	x	x	x		123456				
Apr	x		x	x x x	x	x	x x x	x	123456			
May						x		x	x	123456		
Jun				x x	x x x		x	x x x	x x	x	123456	
Jul	x x x x	x		x	x	x x x	x x x	x x	x x	x	x	123456
Aug			x		x	x					x	x
Sep	x x	x x x				x x	x x x	x x	x x	x x x	x x x	x x
Oct							x	x x x	x	x x	x x	x x
Nov	x										x x x	x x

x: Pellet group no longer present.

87

Appendix 8. Faecal pellet group defecation rate assessment

For all sampling methods it will be necessary to have an estimate of defecation rate for the species being considered to enable deer density to be calculated, based on faecal pellet group counts.

Defecation rate will vary under the influences of sex- and age-class, habitat type and diet (influenced by season). Ideally mean defecation rate should be determined for the population under consideration, by following individual animals of different age- and sex-classes and counting the number of defecations within a given period of time. Mean daily defecation rate can then be calculated. This is rarely practicable and so defecation rates determined from captive animals in similar habitats, or from the literature, are most usually used. For a captive population of known size it is possible to determine defecation rate from clearance plots (14), a knowledge of the number of animals present and the area available to them. This method has been used to determine some of the rates given in Table A8.1.

Table A8.1 *Defecation rates for British deer*

Species	Rate per day	Method of determination	Reference
Red	25 (19-29) (24-33)	clearance plots observations	Mitchell and McCowan, 1984 Mitchell *et al.*, 1983
Sika	25 (26.3) (24)	clearance plots observations	Burkett, unpublished, 1995 Benson, unpublished, 1995
Fallow	21.4	clearance plots	Mayle *et al.*, 1996
Roe	20 (17–23)	clearance plots	Mitchell *et al.*, 1985
Muntjac	7.5	observations	Chapman (personal communication)
Chinese water deer	unknown		

Appendix 9. Plot faecal pellet group count form

Observer's name _____

Forest _____ Location _____

Date _____ Starting point _____ Bearing _____

Structure type _____ Plot area _____

Plot number	1	2	3	4	5	6	7	8	9	10	11	12	Total groups
Dung groups:roe													
Dung groups:red													
Dung groups:fallow													
Dung groups:sika													
Dung groups:muntjac													
Dung groups:roe? muntjac													
Dung groups:roe? fallow													
Dung groups:red? sika													
Dung groups:roe? sheep													

For each species (row)   Total groups [ ] ÷ Number of plots [ ] = [ ] Average number of groups/plot

Appendix 10a. Transect faecal pellet group count form

Record number of pellet groups in each 10 m section of the 1 m wide transect in a separate box.
Pellet groups should be identified to individual deer species.

Transect (m)	10	20	30	40	50	60	70	80	90	100	Total
0-100											
100-200											
200-300											
300-400											
400-500											
											Total=
500-600											
600-700											
700-800											
800-900											
900-1000											
											Total=
1000-1100											
1100-1200											
1200-1300											
1300-1400											
1400-1500											
											Total=
1500-1600											
1600-1700											
1700-1800											
1800-1900											
1900-2000											
											Total=

Appendix 10b. Deer density assessed from transect faecal pellet group count

Table A10.1 *Roe deer density (figures rounded) determined from transect faecal pellet group count*

Dung groups		Deer density
per 500 m transect	per 2000 m transect	per 100 ha
5	20	1.4
10	40	2.7
15	60	4.1
20	80	5.5
25	100	6.8
30	120	8.2
35	140	9.6
40	160	11.0

Density based on a defecation rate of 20 groups per day and a decay rate of 12 months (365 days):

1 Deer = 7300 pellet groups (20 x 365 days)

The relationship for alternative decay rates can be simply calculated by multiplying (x) the deer density by 365 and then dividing (÷) by the new decay rate (days).

Table A10.2 *Red and sika deer densities (figures rounded) determined from transect faecal pellet group count*

Dung groups		Deer density
per 500 m transect	per 2000 m transect	per 100 ha
5	20	1.1
10	40	2.2
15	60	3.3
20	80	4.4
25	100	5.5
30	120	6.6
35	140	7.7
40	160	8.8
45	180	9.9
50	200	11.0

Density based on a defecation rate of 25 groups per day and a decay rate of 12 months (365 days):

1 Deer = 9125 pellet groups (25 x 365 days)

The relationship for alternative decay rates can be simply calculated by multiplying (x) the deer density by 365 and then dividing (÷) by the new decay rate (days).

Appendix 11. Cohort analysis form

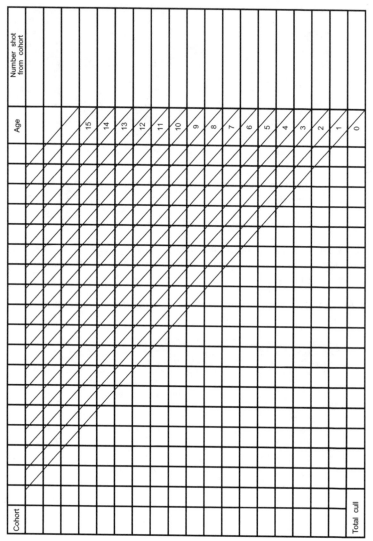

Cohort			Age																Number shot from cohort
			15																
			14																
			13																
			12																
			11																
			10																
			9																
			8																
			7																
			6																
			5																
			4																
			3																
			2																
			1																
			0																
Total cull																			

REFERENCES

Andersen, J. (1953). Analysis of a Danish roe-deer population. *Danish Review of Game Biology* **2**: 127–155.

Bang, P. and Dahlstrom, P. (1974). *Collins guide to animal tracks and signs*. Collins, London.

Boyce, M.S. (1995). Populations and management. In: S.H. Berwick and V.B. Saharia, eds. *The development of international principles and practices of wildlife research and management. Asian and American approaches*. Oxford University press, New Delhi, 263–292.

Buckland, S.T. (1992). Review of deer count methodology. Unpublished report to the Scottish Office.

Buckland, S.T., Anderson, D.R., Burnham, K.P. and Laake, J.L. (1993). *Distance sampling. Estimating abundance of biological populations*. Chapman and Hall, London.

Buckland, S.T., Trenkel, V.M., Elston, D.A., Partridge, L.W. and Gordon, I.J. (1998). A decision support system for red deer managers in Scotland. In: Goldspink, C.R., King, S. and Putman, R.J., eds. *Population ecology, management and welfare of deer*. Manchester Metropolitan University and Universities Federation for Animal Welfare, 82–87.

Bullock, D. J. (1991) . Feral goat. In: Corbet, G.B. and Harris, S., eds. *The handbook of British mammals*. Blackwell Scientific Publications, Oxford, 541–547.

Caughley, G. (1977). *Analysis of vertebrate populations*. Wiley, Chichester.

Chapman N.G. (1991). Muntjac deer. In: Corbet, G.B. and Harris, S., eds. *The handbook of British mammals*. Blackwell Scientific Publications, Oxford, 525–532.

Chapman, D. and Chapman, N.G. (1997). *Fallow deer*. Coch-y-Bonddu Books, Machynlleth, Powys.

Chapman N.G. and Putman, R.J. (1991). Fallow deer. In: Corbet, G.B. and Harris, S., eds. *The handbook of British mammals*. Blackwell Scientific Publications, Oxford, 508–518.

Cochran, W.G. (1977). *Sampling techniques*, 3rd edn. Wiley, New York.

Conner, M.C., Lancia, R.A. and Pollock, K.H. (1986). Precision of the change in ratio technique for deer population management. *Journal of Wildlife Management* **50**: 125–129.

Dzieciolowski, R. (1976). Estimating ungulate numbers in a forest by track counts. *Acta Theriologica* **21**: 217–222.

Farrell, L. and Cooke, A. (1991). Chinese water deer. In: Corbet, G.B. and Harris, S., eds. *The handbook of British mammals*. Blackwell Scientific Publications, Oxford, 532–537.

Ferris-Kaan, R. and Patterson, G.S. (1992). *Monitoring vegetation changes in conservation management of forests.* Forestry Commission Bulletin 108. HMSO, London.

Forestry Authority (1995). *Managing deer in the countryside.* Forestry Practice Advice Note 2. Forestry Commission, Edinburgh.

Gill, R.M.A. (1990). *Monitoring the status of European and North American cervids.* GEMS Information Series No. 8. Global Environment Monitoring System, United Nations Environment Programme, Nairobi, Kenya.

Gill, R.M.A. (1992). A review of damage by mammals in north temperate forests: 1. Deer. *Forestry* **65**(2): 145–169.

Gill, R.M.A., Johnson, A.L., Francis, A., Hiscocks, K. and Peace, A.J. (1996). Changes in roe deer (*Capreolus capreolus* L.) population density in response to forest habitat succession. *Forest Ecology and Management* **88**: 31–41.

Gill, R.M.A., Thomas, M.L. and Stocker, D. (1997). The use of portable thermal imaging for estimating population density in forest habitats. *Journal of Applied Ecology* **34**: 1273–1286.

Greenwood, J.J.D.L. (1996). Basic techniques. In: Sutherland, W.J., ed. *Ecological census techniques.* Cambridge University Press, Cambridge, 11–109.

Harris, S., Morris, P., Wray, S. and Yalden, D. (1995). *A review of British mammals: population estimates and conservation status of British mammals other than cetacean.* JNCC, Peterborough.

Hodge, S. and Pepper, H. (1998). *The prevention of mammal damage to trees in woodland.* Forestry Commission Practice Note 3. Forestry Authority, Edinburgh.

Jewell, P.A. and Bullock, D.J. (1991). In: Corbet, G.B. and Harris, S., eds. *The handbook of British mammals.* Blackwell Scientific Publications, Oxford, 547–552.

Langbein, J. (1996). The red deer of Exmoor and the Quantocks. *Deer* **9**: 492–498.

Leslie, P.H. (1945). On the use of matrices in certain population mathematics. *Biometrika* **33**(3): 183–212.

Leslie, P.H. (1948). Some further notes on the use of matrices in population mathematics. *Biometrika* **35**: 213–245.

Levy, P.S. and Lemeshow, S. (1991). Sampling of populations: methods and applications. *Applied probability and statistics.* Wiley Series in Probability and Mathematical Statistics. Wiley, Chichester.

Lowe, V.P.W. (1969). Population dynamics of the red deer (*Cervus elaphus*) on Rhum. *Journal of Animal Ecology* **38**: 425–457.

Lowe, V.P.W. (1977). Sika deer. In: Corbet, G.B. and Southern, H.N., eds. *The handbook of British mammals*. Blackwell Scientific Publications, Oxford, 423–428.

Mayle, B.A., Doney, J., Lazarus, G., Peace, A.J. and Smith, D.E. (1996). Fallow deer (*Dama dama* L.) defecation rate and its use in determining population size. *Supplemento alle Ricerche di Biologia della Selvaggina* **XXV**, 63–78.

Mitchell, B., McCowan, D. and Campbell, D. (1983). Faecal deposition as indicators of site use by red deer. *Institute of Terrestrial Ecology Annual Report 1982*. ITE, Cambridge, 85–87.

Mitchell, B. and McCowan, D. (1984). The defecation frequencies of red deer in different habitats. *Institute of Terrestrial Ecology Annual Report 1983*. ITE, Cambridge, 15–17.

Mitchell, B. and Kirby, K. (1990). *Forestry* **63**(4): 333–354.

Mitchell, B., Rowe, J.J., Ratcliffe, P.R.R. and Hinge, M. (1985). Defaecation frequency in roe deer (*Capreolus capreolus*) in relation to the accumulation rates of faecal deposits. *Journal of Zoology, London (A)* **207**: 1–7.

Norton-Griffiths, M. (1978). *Counting animals*, 2nd edn. African Wildlife Leadership Foundation, Nairobi. Available from the African Wildlife Foundation, PO Box 48177, Nairobi, Kenya.

Pepper, H.W. (1992). *Forest fencing*. Forestry Commission Bulletin 102. HMSO, London.

Pepper, H.W., Rowe, J.J. and Tee, L.A. (1985). *Individual tree protection*. Arboricultural Leaflet 10. HMSO, London.

Pepper, H.W. (1998). *Nearest neighbour method of quantifying wildlife damage to trees in woodland*. Forestry Commission Practice Note 1. Forestry Authority, Edinburgh.

Pucek, Z., Bobek, B., Labudski, L., Milkowski, L., Morow, K. and Tomek, A. (1975). Estimates of density and numbers of ungulates. *Polish Ecological Studies* **1**: 121–135.

Pyatt, D.G. and Suárez, J.C. (1997). *An ecological site classification for forestry in Great Britain*. Forestry Commission Technical Paper 20. Forestry Commission, Edinburgh.

Ratcliffe, P.R. (1987). The management of red deer in the commercial forests of Scotland related to population dynamics and habitat changes. PhD Thesis, London.

Ratcliffe, P.R. (1991). Sika deer. In: Corbet, G.B. and Harris, S., eds. *The handbook of British mammals*. Blackwell Scientific Publications, Oxford, 504–508.

Ratcliffe, P.R. and Mayle, B.A. (1992). *Roe deer biology and management*. Forestry Commission Bulletin 105. HMSO, London.

Reynolds, P., Duck, C., Youngson, D. and Clem, D. (1994). An evaluation of airborne thermal imaging for the census of red deer (*Cervus elephus*) populations in extensive open habitats in Scotland. In: *Forests and wildlife - towards the 21st century.* Proceedings of 21st International Union of Game Biologists Congress, Halifax, Nova Scotia, Canada 1993. Canadian Forest Service, Petawawa National Forestry Institute, Chalk River, Ontario, vol. 2, 162–168.

Smith, D.F.E. and Mayle, B.A. (1994). Fallow deer density and habitat use at Coed-Y-Brenin. Unpublished Forestry Commission Research Division closure report.

Staines, B.W. (1991). Red deer. In: Corbet, G.B. and Harris, S., eds. *The handbook of British mammals.* Blackwell Scientific Publications, Oxford, 492–504.

Staines, B.W. and Ratcliffe, P.R. (1991). Roe deer. In: Corbet, G.B. and Harris, S., eds. *The handbook of British mammals.* Blackwell Scientific Publications, Oxford, 518–525.

Stewart, L.K. (1976). The Scottish red deer census. *Deer* 3(10): 529–533.

Strandgaard, H. (1972). The roe deer (*Capreolus capreolus* L.) population at Kalo and the factors regulating its size. *Danish Review of Game Biology* 7: 1–205.

Sutherland, W.J. (1996). *Ecological census techniques.* Cambridge University Press, Cambridge, 336.

Thompson, S.K. (1992). *Sampling. Applied probability and statistics.* Wiley Series in Probability and Mathematical Statistics. Wiley, Chichester.

White, G.C. and Garrott, R.A. (1990). *Analysis of wildlife radio-tracking data.* Academic Press, London.